Higher
GCSE MATHS 4–9

Homework Book

Michael White

Elmwood Education

First published 2015 by
Elmwood Education Ltd
Unit 5, Mallow Park
Watchmead
Welwyn Garden City
AL7 1GX
Tel. 01707 333232

ISBN 9781 906 622 466

Typeset and illustrated by Tech-Set Ltd., Gateshead, Tyne and Wear.

CONTENTS

UNIT 6

Algebra 2

UNIT 8

Statistics 1

UNIT 9

Geometry 2

UNIT 10

Geometry 3

UNIT 11

Statistics 2

UNIT 12

Algebra 3

UNIT 13

Geometry 4

UNIT 14

Statistics 3

UNIT 16

Algebra 4

UNIT 17

Geometry 5

UNIT 18

Geometry 6

NUMBER 1

| **TASK M1.1** | **Main Book Page 1** |

Do not use a calculator.

1 Find the value of each calculation below:

a $\dfrac{16 - 4}{2 + 4}$

b $\dfrac{3^2 + 4^2}{10 - 5}$

c $\dfrac{(11 + 4) \times (18 - 13)}{5^2}$

d $\sqrt{(5^2 + 12^2)}$

e $\dfrac{4 \times 4 + 4}{4 \times 10}$

f $\dfrac{6 + 9 \div 3}{(19 + 17) \div 4}$

2 36 people pay a total of £936 to visit the theatre. If each person pays the same amount, how much does each person pay?

3 250 football supporters from the same town travel to an away match. Four full coaches are used, costing £408 each. Each coach holds 54 people. The remaining people pay £17 each to travel by train.
If one extra coach had been used for the remaining people so they did not travel by train, how much money would each of the remaining people have saved?

4 Write down the answer to each of the following:

a 0.4×0.6 　　**b** 0.07×0.5 　　**c** $6 - 1.03$ 　　**d** 20×0.06

e 0.3^2 　　**f** $0.81 \div 0.3$ 　　**g** $5.7 \div 0.03$ 　　**h** 1.8×15

i 0.36×2.7 　　**j** 0.02^3 　　**k** $0.6 \div 0.003$ 　　**l** 600×0.12

5 How many 0·45 litre cartons of milk are needed to give 5·4 litres in total?

6 Croissants are loaded into trays of 32. How many trays are used to deal with 1400 croissants?

7 Which is larger? or

8 A box of crisps contains 48 packets. Janine buys 263 boxes.
She pays 35p for each packet of crisps. She sells all the crisps at 60p per packet except for 150 packets which are damaged so cannot be sold.
How much profit does she make if she has additional overhead costs of £1641·12?

| **TASK M1.2** | **Main Book Page 3** |

1 Work out and give the answer in its simplest form:

a $\dfrac{5}{8} \times \dfrac{8}{9}$

b $\dfrac{7}{12} \times \dfrac{3}{14}$

c $\dfrac{3}{4} \times 20$

d $\dfrac{3}{5} \div \dfrac{9}{10}$

e $\dfrac{4}{9} \div \dfrac{1}{3}$

f $2\dfrac{1}{2} \times \dfrac{7}{10}$

g $3\dfrac{1}{3} \times 1\dfrac{4}{5}$

h $6\dfrac{1}{4} \div 1\dfrac{3}{7}$

2 Gary gives $\frac{2}{3}$ of his money to Carol. Carol gives $\frac{6}{7}$ of this money to Zak.

What fraction of Gary's money does Zak get?

3 Work out and give the answer in its simplest form:

a $\frac{1}{4} + \frac{2}{3}$ **b** $\frac{5}{6} - \frac{3}{8}$ **c** $3\frac{3}{4} + 1\frac{5}{12}$ **d** $5\frac{1}{3} - \frac{7}{8}$

4 How many minutes longer does it take Denise to complete a job in three-quarters of an hour than Simon who completes the job in five-twelfths of an hour?

5 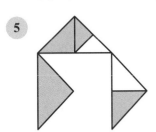 Three congruent triangles are joined together as shown opposite. Parts of the triangles are shaded grey.

One more congruent triangle is added to these triangles. Half of this extra triangle is shaded grey.

What fraction of all the four congruent triangles is shaded grey?

6 Annie and Chad walk from a pub in the same direction. If Annie has walked five-eighths of a mile and Chad has walked seven-tenths of a mile, how far apart are they?

7 Work out and give the answer in its simplest form:

a $\frac{1}{4} \times \frac{6}{7} + \frac{1}{2}$ **b** $\frac{8}{9} \div \frac{2}{3} - \frac{1}{6}$ **c** $\left(3\frac{2}{3} - 2\frac{3}{5}\right) \div \frac{2}{5}$

8 A piece of paper measures $8\frac{1}{4}$ cm by $7\frac{1}{3}$ cm. A square of side $2\frac{1}{2}$ cm is cut out and thrown away. Show that the area that is left is exactly $54\frac{1}{4}$ cm².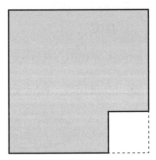

9 A photo measures $7\frac{1}{2}$ cm by $7\frac{1}{5}$ cm. Both its dimensions are increased by a factor of $1\frac{1}{3}$. Find the area of the enlarged photo.

10 Rahul increases the size of his lawn by one-fifth. His lawn now has an area of 108 m². What was the area of his lawn before he made it larger?

TASK M1.3   **Main Book Page 6**

Use a calculator.

1 Each of the calculations below is wrong. Find the correct answer for each calculation.

a $\frac{48 + 32}{20} = 49{\cdot}6$ **b** $\frac{51 - 31}{10} = 47{\cdot}9$ **c** $\frac{50}{25 \times 10} = 20$ **d** $\frac{75}{40 - 20} = -18{\cdot}125$

2 Work out the following, giving answers to the *nearest whole number*. Match each calculation to the correct answer.

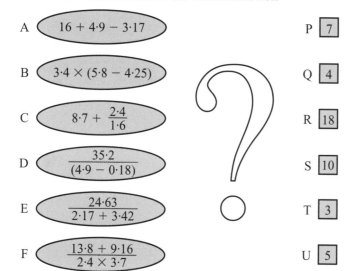

A $16 + 4\cdot9 - 3\cdot17$

B $3\cdot4 \times (5\cdot8 - 4\cdot25)$

C $8\cdot7 + \dfrac{2\cdot4}{1\cdot6}$

D $\dfrac{35\cdot2}{(4\cdot9 - 0\cdot18)}$

E $\dfrac{24\cdot63}{2\cdot17 + 3\cdot42}$

F $\dfrac{13\cdot8 + 9\cdot16}{2\cdot4 \times 3\cdot7}$

P $\boxed{7}$

Q $\boxed{4}$

R $\boxed{18}$

S $\boxed{10}$

T $\boxed{3}$

U $\boxed{5}$

3 A Bureau de Change offers $\$1\cdot568$ per £ but charges a commission fee of £3. How many dollars (to the nearest cent) do you get for £75?

4 Which is larger? A $\left(3\tfrac{2}{5}\right)^2$ or B $20\tfrac{1}{4} \div 1\tfrac{7}{9}$

5 Write the numbers below in order of size, starting with the smallest.

$\boxed{3^4}$ $\boxed{2^7}$ $\boxed{5^3}$ $\boxed{1^9}$ $\boxed{4^4}$

6 Calculate the following, giving each answer to 3 significant figures.

a $\dfrac{17\cdot2 + 8\cdot16}{8\cdot61 - 2\cdot48}$

b $3\sqrt{8} - 5$

c $\dfrac{(-9\cdot1)^2 + 7\cdot13}{(-4\cdot28)^2}$

d $\dfrac{\sqrt{8} + \sqrt{2}}{\sqrt{7} - \sqrt{3}}$

e $\dfrac{-7\cdot3 + (-1\cdot9)^2}{(-1\cdot72) \times (-2\cdot4)}$

f $(\sqrt{6} - \sqrt{8})^4$

7 The area of mould on a slice of bread is 1 cm² after 4 days. One day later the area has increased by one third of this size. It then increases by two-fifths of its new size by the end of day 6. It then increases by two-thirds of its new size by the end of day 7. Calculate the area of the mould after one week.

8

$x \xrightarrow{+} \boxed{2\tfrac{1}{4}} \xrightarrow{\times} \boxed{\tfrac{4}{5}} \xrightarrow{-} \boxed{1\tfrac{1}{3}} \xrightarrow{\div} \boxed{\tfrac{1}{2}} = \boxed{4\tfrac{46}{75}}$

Work out the value of x.

9 A rugby player weighs $15\tfrac{1}{2}$ stones. *Roughly* how much does the player weigh in kilograms? Research the conversions and show your working out.

4

1 Convert the decimals below into fractions in their lowest form.

    a 0·7   **b** 0·35   **c** 0·035   **d** 0·92

    e 0·618   **f** 0·3185   **g** 0·713   **h** 0·625

2 By changing each fraction into a decimal, write the following fractions in order of size, starting with the smallest.

$$\frac{3}{20} \qquad \frac{1}{4} \qquad \frac{3}{10} \qquad \frac{5}{16} \qquad \frac{3}{25} \qquad \frac{45}{200}$$

3 Use division to convert the fractions below into recurring decimals:

    a $\dfrac{2}{9}$ **b** $\dfrac{5}{12}$ **c** $\dfrac{5}{6}$ **d** $\dfrac{5}{13}$ **e** $\dfrac{6}{7}$

4 Convert $\dfrac{137}{999}$ into a recurring decimal.

1 Copy and complete to change $0·7\dot{4}$ to a fraction.

        let f = 0·74 74 74 …

      100f = ☐

    we have f = 0·74 74 74 …

    subtract

        99f = ☐

          f = $\dfrac{☐}{☐}$

2 Express the following recurring decimals as fractions in their lowest form:

    a $0·\dot{7}$ **b** $0·\dot{2}\dot{8}$ **c** 0·646464 …

    d $0·3\dot{8}\dot{2}$ **e** 0·57777 …   **f** $5·6\dot{8}\dot{4}$

3 Express $0·7\dot{1}\dot{5}$ in the form $\dfrac{a}{b}$ where a and b are integers (whole numbers).

1 $\sqrt{12} = \sqrt{4 \times 3} = \sqrt{4}\sqrt{3} = 2\sqrt{3}$. This is the simplified answer.
    Simplify

    a $\sqrt{18}$ **b** $\sqrt{32}$ **c** $\sqrt{72}$ **d** $\sqrt{20}$

    e $\sqrt{125}$ **f** $\sqrt{28}$ **g** $\sqrt{300}$ **h** $\sqrt{54}$

2 Which of the statements below are true?

   a $\sqrt{14} \div \sqrt{2} = \sqrt{7}$ **b** $\sqrt{18} - \sqrt{8} = \sqrt{10}$ **c** $\sqrt{5} + \sqrt{9} = \sqrt{14}$

3 Simplify as far as possible

   a $\sqrt{7} \times \sqrt{5}$ **b** $\sqrt{2} \times \sqrt{5} \times \sqrt{3}$ **c** $(\sqrt{7})^2$

   d $\sqrt{32} \div \sqrt{8}$ **e** $\dfrac{\sqrt{12}}{\sqrt{6}}$ **f** $\dfrac{\sqrt{30}}{\sqrt{5}}$

   g $3\sqrt{2} \times 6\sqrt{3}$ **h** $2\sqrt{5} \times 4\sqrt{2}$ **i** $(2\sqrt{7})^2$

4 Simplify as far as possible

   a $7\sqrt{3} - 5\sqrt{3}$ **b** $3\sqrt{5} + 3\sqrt{5}$ **c** $5\sqrt{2} - \sqrt{18}$

   d $4\sqrt{2} + \sqrt{8}$ **e** $7\sqrt{6} - \sqrt{24}$ **f** $\sqrt{8} + \sqrt{50}$

   g $\sqrt{80} - \sqrt{45}$ **h** $2\sqrt{5} \times 2\sqrt{5}$ **i** $5\sqrt{2} \times 3\sqrt{2} \times 4\sqrt{2}$

   j $\sqrt{63} - \sqrt{28}$ **k** $\sqrt{75} + \sqrt{12} - \sqrt{108}$ **l** $(2\sqrt{3})^3$

5 Solve

   a $\sqrt{3} \times \sqrt{n} = \sqrt{21}$ **b** $\sqrt{7} \times \sqrt{n} = 14$ **c** $3\sqrt{n} \times \sqrt{5} = 15$

6 Simplify

   a $\sqrt{n} \times \sqrt{n}$ **b** $m\sqrt{n} \times p\sqrt{n}$ **c** $\dfrac{m\sqrt{n} \times p\sqrt{n}}{q\sqrt{n}}$

TASK E1.3	**Main Book Page 14**

1 Prove that $(\sqrt{3} + \sqrt{2})(\sqrt{3} - \sqrt{2}) = 1$.

2 Prove that $(\sqrt{5} + \sqrt{2})(\sqrt{5} + \sqrt{2}) = 7 + 2\sqrt{10}$.

3 Expand and simplify

   a $(\sqrt{2} + 5)(\sqrt{3} + 2)$ **b** $(\sqrt{3} + \sqrt{7})(\sqrt{5} + \sqrt{2})$ **c** $(\sqrt{8} - \sqrt{5})(\sqrt{2} + \sqrt{3})$

   d $(\sqrt{6} - 1)(\sqrt{6} + 1)$ **e** $(\sqrt{3} + 4)^2$ **f** $(\sqrt{7} - \sqrt{5})^2$

4 Find the 'exact' value of

   a the area of this rectangle

   b the perimeter of this rectangle.

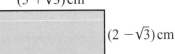

$(5 + \sqrt{3})\,\mathrm{cm}$

$(2 - \sqrt{3})\,\mathrm{cm}$

5 $(3 + \sqrt{5})\,\mathrm{cm}$

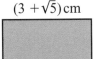

   The perimeter of this rectangle is $(8 + 6\sqrt{5})\,\mathrm{cm}$.
   Find the 'exact' value of the area of the rectangle.

6 Prove that $(\sqrt{a} + \sqrt{b})(\sqrt{a} - \sqrt{b}) = a - b$.

7 *Explain* why $(\sqrt{a} - \sqrt{b})^2$ is *not* $a - b$.

8 Write down two surds which divide to give an integer answer.

TASK E1.4 ──────────────────────────── **Main Book Page 16**

1 Rationalise the denominator in each of the following:

   a $\dfrac{1}{\sqrt{6}}$ **b** $\dfrac{2}{\sqrt{3}}$ **c** $\dfrac{\sqrt{3}}{\sqrt{7}}$

   d $\dfrac{4\sqrt{5}}{\sqrt{3}}$ **e** $\dfrac{\sqrt{5} - \sqrt{2}}{\sqrt{3}}$ **f** $\dfrac{\sqrt{3} + 1}{\sqrt{5}}$

2 **a** Expand $(2 + \sqrt{3})(2 - \sqrt{3})$

    b Rationalise the denominator of $\dfrac{5}{2 + \sqrt{3}}$

3 Simplify the following as far as possible:

   a $\sqrt{8} \times \sqrt{6}$ **b** $\sqrt{15} \times \sqrt{5}$ **c** $\dfrac{21}{\sqrt{7}}$

   d $3\sqrt{3}(\sqrt{2} - \sqrt{3})$ **e** $\sqrt{8} - \dfrac{2}{\sqrt{2}}$ **f** $(\sqrt{6} - 2)^2$

   g $\sqrt{12} + \dfrac{9}{\sqrt{3}}$ **h** $(\sqrt{5} - \sqrt{3})(\sqrt{3} + \sqrt{2})$ **i** $(\sqrt{7} - 2)(\sqrt{7} + 2)$

   j $(\sqrt{3} + 5)^3$ **k** $4\sqrt{3}(1 + \sqrt{5})$ **l** $\dfrac{\sqrt{45} - 3}{\sqrt{5} - 1}$

4 Use Pythagoras to find the value of x, leaving the answer in surd form.
All lengths are in cm.

   a 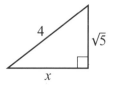   **b**   **c**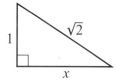

5 Prove that $\sqrt{a} + \sqrt{b} = \sqrt{(a + b)}$ is *not* true if $a \neq 0$ and/or $b \neq 0$ ($\neq$ means 'not equal to').

6 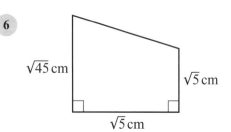   Work out the 'exact' perimeter
of this trapezium.

7   Prove that $\dfrac{\sqrt{3}}{2} \times \dfrac{1}{\sqrt{2}} + \dfrac{1}{2} \times \dfrac{1}{\sqrt{2}} = \dfrac{\sqrt{6} + \sqrt{2}}{4}$

8   Leah says that $\left(2 + \dfrac{1}{\sqrt{3}}\right)^2 + \left(1 - \dfrac{2}{\sqrt{3}}\right)^2 > 7$.

   Is she correct? Justify your answer without using a calculator.

NUMBER 2   2

TASK M2.1 ────────────────────────── **Main Book Page 26**

Use a calculator when needed. Give answers to the nearest penny when needed.

1   A tin of baked beans costs 42p. Its price increases by 9% over the next 12 months. How much will the tin cost now? (remember to give your answer to the nearest penny)

2   A new car exhaust costs £88 + VAT. If VAT is 20%, work out the total cost of the car exhaust.

3   Write down the percentage multiplier that could be used for the following (eg. 'increase of 4%' means the percentage multiplier is 1·04).

   a   increase of 15%   b   decrease of 7%   c   decrease of 42%

   d   increase of 8·5%   e   reduction of 24%   f   increase of 17·5%

4   If VAT is 20%, find the price including VAT of each of the following:

   a | microwave £126 | b | carpet £870 |

   c | digital camera £220 | d | kettle £34 |

5   VAT on a gas bill is charged at 5%. Cooper's gas bill for this quarter is £185 + VAT. If the Government decided to change the VAT rate to the standard 20%, how much *more* would Cooper have to pay for this quarter's bill?

6   90% of the spectators at a football game support the home team and the remaining spectators support the away team. 60% of the home fans walk to the ground and 20% of the away fans walk to the ground. What percentage of the spectators did *not* walk to the ground?

7   An eternity ring costs £680 + VAT (20%). In the Summer sales, the price of the ring is reduced by 20%. How much does the ring cost in the sales?

SALE
20% OFF
ALL PRICES

8 ⬭ HATS £2

BALLOONS £1

Stella sells hats and balloons at a carnival. 120 hats cost her 50p each and 150 balloons cost her 15p each.

During the carnival she sells 40 hats at £2 each. She then reduces the hat price by 25% and sells a further 60 hats. She sells 50 balloons at £1 each then offers a 50% reduction and sells a further 30 balloons. She then reduces the new price by 50% and sells another 45 balloons. Work out how much profit Stella makes in total.

9 The price of a TV is increased by 30% then the new price is decreased by 30%. What is the overall percentage change to the original price of the TV?

| TASK M2.2 | Main Book Page 29 |

Use a calculator when needed. Give answers to one decimal place if necessary.

1 Ryan buys a mobile for £240 and sells it one year later for £204.
What was his percentage loss?

2 Kelly buys a car for £300 and works on it before selling it for £420.
What was the percentage profit?

3 A supermarket increases its workforce from 90 people to 117 people.
What is the percentage increase?

4 Find the percentage increase or decrease for each of the following:

a | original amount = 360   final amount = 514·8

b | original amount = 672   final amount = 564·48

c | original amount = 32   final amount = 62·4

5 Leanne buys 100 books for £450. She sells each book for £5·40.
Find the percentage profit Leanne makes on the books.

6 Sam buys 70 scarves at £5 each. He sells 40 of the scarves for £11 each but fails to sell the other scarves. Find the percentage profit he makes.

7 Joe buys a flat for £70 000 and sells it for £85 000.
Mo buys a house for £192 000 and sells it for £230 000.
Who makes the larger percentage profit and by how much?

8 The length, width and height of this cuboid are each increased by 15%.
What is the percentage increase in the volume of this cuboid?

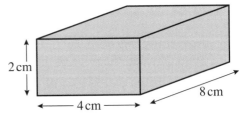

2 cm

4 cm

8 cm

9 Last year 160 students out of 240 in Year 11 in Henton High School attained a grade 4 or above in their Maths GCSE. This year there was a 10% increase in the number of people gaining a grade 4 or above for GCSE Maths. The number of students in Year 11 increased by 5% compared to last year. Work out the percentage increase in the pass rate this year compared to last year for students in Year 11 gaining a grade 4 or above in GCSE Maths.

10 Sandra's ideal body weight is 57 kg. During a period of six months her weight increases by 10%. During the next three months her weight returns to its ideal 57 kg. What was the percentage decrease from her heaviest weight back to her ideal weight?

| TASK M2.3 | Main Book Page 31 |

Use a calculator when needed. Give answers to the nearest penny if necessary.

1 Tina invests £8000 in a bank at 5% per annum (year) compound interest. How much money will she have in the bank after 2 years?

2 A motorbike loses 25% of its value every year. Jennifer bought it for £720. How much would it be worth after:

a 2 years   **b** 3 years

3 Which of the following will earn more money in 2 years?

A £4000 at 5·6% p.a. *simple* interest   *or*   **B** £4000 at 5·5% p.a. compound interest

4 A building society offers 8% p.a. compound interest. Candice puts £560 into the building society.

a Write down the *percentage multiplier* which could be used to find out how much money is in the building society after 1 year.

b How much money would be in the building society after 5 years?

5

Supa Save

4% per annum compound interest plus 2% bonus at the end of 3 years

Mega Money

4·5% per annum compound interest

Robert has £15 000 to invest for 3 years. Which account above will give him more money and by how much?

6 In a large town, 30 000 people get their gas supply from Central Gas. 10 000 people get their gas from Gas Centric.

By the end of each year, Central Gas lose 10% of their customers at the start of the year and Gas Centric gain 15% of their customers at the start of the year. During which year does Gas Centric first have more customers than Central Gas? *Explain* your answer fully.

7 Vikram invests some money in a bank at 12% p.a. compound interest. After how many years will his money have trebled?

8 Mrs Jones is 65 years old. She has worked out that due to inflation her savings will lose 5% of their value at the start of each year by the end of that year.

How old will she be by the end of the first year in which her savings are worth less than half of their current value?

| **TASK M2.4** | **Main Book Page 34** |

Use a calculator when needed.

1 Ron's height has increased by 5% over the last year. He is now 1·89 m tall.
How tall was he one year ago?

2 Katy now pays £129·60 rent each week after an 8% rent increase.
How much did she pay before the increase?

3 One week Arlene spends £75·60 on food which is 18% of her weekly pay.
How much is her weekly pay?

4 A bike costs £408 including VAT at 20%. How much did the bike cost before VAT was added?

5 46 students from Year 10 in Grove Park School are ill one day. If this is 28·75% of all the Year 10 pupils, how many students are there in Year 10 in total?

6

| DVD player £61 including VAT | In which shop is the DVD player cheaper and by how much? (VAT is 20%) | DVD player £52 + VAT |

HOBB'S ELECTRICS   HEFTON'S

7 Council Tax is increased by 3% each year for two consecutive years. The Harris family pay £1350 in the year after the two rises. How much did they pay two years earlier?

8 The number of people working in a factory in 2013 drops 20% by 2014. This number then increases 25% by the year 2015. In 2015 there are 90 people working in the factory. What overall percentage change in the number of people has taken place between 2013 and 2015?

9 Don answers the following question:

'A computer is sold for £1200 at a loss of 20%.
How much was the computer originally bought for?'

Don answers as follows:

Loss is 20% of £1200 = 0·2 × 1200 = £240

Original price = 1200 + 240 = £1440

Explain clearly the mistakes in Don's answer.

10 The price of a barrel of oil falls 14% then increases by 10%. The current price is £96·49 per barrel. What was the price of a barrel before the two percentage changes?

11 A cube is coated with a varnish which increases the length of each side by $\frac{1}{2}$%. The volume of the cube including varnish is now $219 \cdot 256\,227\,\text{cm}^3$. What was the volume of the original cube?

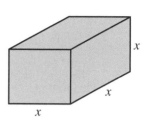

TASK M2.5 — Main Book Page 37

1 Change the following ratios to their simplest form.

   a $32:28$ **b** $12:9:21$ **c** $50\,\text{cm}:4\,\text{m}$ **d** $25\text{p}:£3$ **e** $\frac{4}{5}:\frac{1}{3}$

2 The angles p, q and r are in the ratio $7:2:3$.
Find the sizes of angles p, q and r.

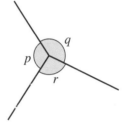

3 The ratio of boys to girls in a class is $6:5$.
How many girls are there in the class if there are 18 boys?

4 Paint is mixed by using yellow and blue in the ratio $7:2$.

   a How much yellow is used if 8 litres of blue are used?

   b How much blue is used if 35 litres of yellow are used?

   c How much yellow and how much blue must be used to make 72 litres of the paint?

5 Des, Simone and Julie earn money in the ratio $3:2:5$. If Des earns £9000 per year more than Simone, how much does Julie earn each year?

6 Cheese kebabs for 4 people need the ingredients below:

220 g	cheese
4	tomatos
8	pineapple chunks
$\frac{1}{2}$	cucumber

How much of each ingredient is needed for 10 people?

7 The recipe for making 20 biscuits is given below:

120 g	butter
50 g	caster sugar
175 g	flour

Helen has 300 g butter, 200 g caster sugar and 525 g flour. What is the maximum number of biscuits she can make?

8 m is $\frac{3}{8}$ of n. Write down the ratio $m:n$.

9 The area of a garden is $40\,\text{m}^2$. It is split into a lawn and flower beds in the ratio $4:1$.
Eva decides to grow vegetables so splits the lawn into a vegetable patch and lawn in the ratio
$2:3$. Work out the area of the vegetable patch.

10 5 litres of antifreeze and water are mixed together in the ratio $1:3$. How much water must be
added to make the ratio $1:5$?

11 $PQ:QR:RS = 7:3:8$
If PQ is $10\,\text{cm}$ longer than QR,
what is the length of line PS?

P ———————————————— Q ———— R —— S

TASK M2.6 | **Main Book Page 40**

1 Work out and write each answer as a number in index form:

a $3^8 \div 3^3$ **b** $2^3 \times 2^4 \times 2^2$ **c** $5^3 \times 5 \times 5^3$

d $5^6 \times 5^2 \div 5^4$ **e** $(4^2)^3$ **f** 8^0

g $\dfrac{3^6 \times 3^4}{3^7}$ **h** $6^2 \times (6^2)^2$ **i** $\dfrac{7^4 \times (7^3)^2}{7^5}$

> **Remember:**
> $a^m \times a^n = a^{m+n}$
> $(a^m)^n = a^{mn}$
> $a^m \div a^n = a^{m-n}$
> $a^0 = 1$

2 Copy and complete:

a $3^4 \times \boxed{} = 3^9$ **b** $\boxed{} \times 6^3 = 6^7$ **c** $5^7 \div \boxed{} = 5^2$

d $8^{12} \div \boxed{} = 8^{11}$ **e** $\boxed{} \div 4^6 = 4^2$ **f** $(7^2)^3 \div \boxed{} = 7^2$

3 Simplify the expressions below:

a $x^4 \times x^3$ **b** $(x^2)^4$ **c** $a^6 \div a^2$

d $(a^0)^3$ **e** $(x^3)^2 \div x^2$ **f** $x^5 \div x$

4 Answer true or false for each statement below:

a $(x^4)^5 = x^9$ **b** $y^4 \times y^2 = y^8$ **c** $x^3 \times x = x^3$

d $\dfrac{n^6}{n} = n^5$ **e** $\dfrac{(x^3)^3}{(x^2)^3} = x^3$ **f** $\dfrac{(a^2)^4}{a} = a^6$

5 Simplify the expressions below:

a $\dfrac{(x^2)^6 \times x^2}{(x^7)^2}$ **b** $\dfrac{m^9}{m^2 \times m^5}$ **c** $\dfrac{n^{10}}{(n^3)^2 \times n^2}$

d $\dfrac{(x^3)^4 \times (x^2)^5}{(x^3)^6}$ **e** $\dfrac{m^{19}}{(m^2)^4 \times (m^5)^2}$ **f** $\dfrac{(x^3)^3 \times (x^2)^5}{(x^6)^2 \times (x^2)^2}$

6 Which of the following expressions is the odd one out?

$6a^2 \times 4a^5$

$3a \times 2a^3 \times 4a^3$

$8a^2 \times a^3 \times 3a$

$2a^3 \times 12(a^2)^2$

7 Answer true or false for each statement below:

a $3x \times 3x = 9x^2$　　　**b** $5x^2 \times 4x^3 = 20x^6$　　　**c** $(3a^2)^2 = 9a^4$

d $\dfrac{15x^7}{3x^4} = 5x^3$　　　**e** $\dfrac{20(x^3)^2}{10(x^2)^3} = 10$　　　**f** $(8a)^2 \times 8a^2 = 64a^4$

8 Simplify the expressions below:

a $3a^2 \times 2a^5$　　　**b** $(4b^2)^2$　　　**c** $\dfrac{40x^{10}}{5x^4}$

d $63m^7 \div 7m^5$　　　**e** $-9y^3 \times 4y^2$　　　**f** $(4n^3)^2$

TASK M2.7 ——————————————————————— **Main Book Page 42**

1 3^{-2} (index form) $= \dfrac{1}{3^2} = \dfrac{1}{9}$ (ordinary number)

Write the following as ordinary numbers:

> **Remember:**
> $a^{-n} = \dfrac{1}{a^n}$

a 4^{-1}　　　**b** 2^{-3}　　　**c** 6^{-2}　　　**d** 4^{-3}

e 10^{-2}　　　**f** 5^{-3}　　　**g** 7^{-1}　　　**h** 2^{-6}

2 Write the following in negative index form:

a $\dfrac{1}{4^2}$　　　**b** $\dfrac{1}{3^4}$　　　**c** $\dfrac{1}{2^5}$　　　**d** $\dfrac{1}{8^3}$

3 Write $\dfrac{1}{25}$ as a power of 5 in negative index form.

4 Write $\dfrac{1}{27}$ as a power of 3 in negative index form.

5 Answer true or false for each statement below:

a $2^{-8} = \dfrac{1}{2^8}$　　　**b** $6^{-2} \times 6^{-2} = 6^{-4}$　　　**c** $9^{-1} = -9$

d $3^{-5} = \dfrac{5}{3}$　　　**e** $\left(\dfrac{1}{4}\right)^{-1} = 4$　　　**f** $\left(\dfrac{2}{3}\right)^{-2} = \dfrac{9}{4}$

6 Work out the sum of the reciprocal of 4 and the reciprocal of 5.

7 Find the reciprocal of $\dfrac{1}{6}n$.

8 Simplify the expressions below:

a $\dfrac{x^3 \times x^{-1}}{x^{-4}}$　　　**b** $(5x^{-3})^2$　　　**c** $\dfrac{4m^2 \times 3m^{-5}}{6m^{-2}}$

9 Write the following as ordinary numbers:

a $\left(\dfrac{1}{3}\right)^{-1}$ **b** $\left(\dfrac{3}{7}\right)^{-1}$ **c** $\left(\dfrac{3}{5}\right)^{-2}$ **d** $\left(\dfrac{2}{7}\right)^{-2}$

10 Is the reciprocal of a number x always smaller than the number x?
Explain your answer fully.

TASK E2.1   **Main Book Page 45**

Do not use a calculator.

> **Remember:**
> $a^{\frac{1}{n}} = \sqrt[n]{a}$

1 Evaluate the following:

a $25^{\frac{1}{2}}$ **b** $64^{\frac{1}{3}}$ **c** $1^{\frac{1}{3}}$ **d** $4^{-\frac{1}{2}}$

e $8^{-\frac{1}{3}}$ **f** $16^{\frac{1}{4}}$ **g** $100^{-\frac{1}{2}}$ **h** $216^{\frac{1}{3}}$

2 Express the following as powers of 16:

a 4   **b** 1   **c** $\dfrac{1}{2}$ **d** $\dfrac{1}{16}$

3 Simplify the following:

a $\sqrt{x^6}$ **b** $(x^6)^{\frac{1}{2}}$ **c** $(x^6)^{\frac{1}{3}}$

d $\sqrt{25x^4}$ **e** $\sqrt[3]{8n^6}$ **f** $(27m^{12})^{\frac{1}{3}}$

g $(9a^6)^{-\frac{1}{2}}$ **h** $(64m^9)^{-\frac{1}{3}}$ **i** $(49a^2b^6)^{\frac{1}{2}}$

4 Evaluate the following:

a $121^{-\frac{1}{2}}$ **b** $\left(\dfrac{16}{25}\right)^{\frac{1}{2}}$ **c** $\left(\dfrac{81}{64}\right)^{-\frac{1}{2}}$ **d** $\left(\dfrac{9}{4}\right)^{-\frac{1}{2}}$

e $\left(\dfrac{8}{125}\right)^{\frac{1}{3}}$ **f** $\left(\dfrac{27}{64}\right)^{-\frac{1}{3}}$ **g** $\left(\dfrac{1}{216}\right)^{-\frac{1}{3}}$ **h** $\left(\dfrac{81}{10\,000}\right)^{-\frac{1}{4}}$

5 Which of the following expressions is the odd one out?

$\left(\dfrac{1}{9a^2b^4}\right)^{-\frac{1}{2}}$ $(27a^3b^6)^{\frac{1}{3}}$ $(81a^4b^{12})^{\frac{1}{4}}$ $(9a^2b^4)^{\frac{1}{2}}$

TASK E2.2   **Main Book Page 47**

> **Remember:** $a^{\frac{m}{n}} = \sqrt[n]{a^m}$ or $a^{\frac{m}{n}} = (\sqrt[n]{a})^m$

Do not use a calculator in the questions that follow.

1 Copy and complete the following:

a $16^{\frac{3}{2}}$

$= \left(16^{\frac{1}{2}}\right)^3$

$= \left(\boxed{}\right)^3$

$= \boxed{}$

b $8^{-\frac{2}{3}}$

$= \dfrac{1}{\boxed{}^{\frac{2}{3}}}$

$= \dfrac{1}{\left(\boxed{}^{\frac{1}{3}}\right)^2}$

$= \dfrac{1}{\boxed{}^2}$

$= \dfrac{1}{\boxed{}}$

c $\left(\dfrac{25}{49}\right)^{-\frac{3}{2}}$

$= \left(\dfrac{\boxed{}}{\boxed{}}\right)^{\frac{3}{2}}$

$= \left(\dfrac{\boxed{}^{\frac{1}{2}}}{\boxed{}^{\frac{1}{2}}}\right)^{\boxed{}}$

$= \left(\dfrac{\boxed{}}{\boxed{}}\right)^{\boxed{}} = \dfrac{\boxed{}}{\boxed{}}$

2 Evaluate the following:

a $36^{\frac{3}{2}}$

b $25^{\frac{3}{2}}$

c $16^{-\frac{3}{4}}$

d $125^{\frac{2}{3}}$

e $1000^{-\frac{2}{3}}$

f $81^{\frac{3}{4}}$

g $4^{-\frac{3}{2}}$

h $64^{-\frac{2}{3}}$

3 Simplify the following:

a $(4x^4)^{\frac{3}{2}}$

b $(27m^9)^{\frac{2}{3}}$

c $\sqrt{x} \times x\sqrt{x}$

d $\left(\dfrac{x^3}{8y^6}\right)^{-\frac{2}{3}}$

e $(16a^8b^4)^{\frac{3}{4}}$

f $(64m^{12}n^9)^{\frac{2}{3}}$

4 Evaluate the following:

a $\left(\dfrac{8}{27}\right)^{-\frac{2}{3}}$

b $\left(\dfrac{81}{16}\right)^{-\frac{3}{4}}$

c $\left(\dfrac{25}{4}\right)^{-\frac{3}{2}}$

d $\left(\dfrac{125}{64}\right)^{-\frac{2}{3}}$

5 Which of the statements below are true?

a $8^{-\frac{2}{3}} = \dfrac{1}{4}$

b $\left(\dfrac{16}{49}\right)^{-\frac{1}{2}} = -\dfrac{4}{7}$

c $\left(\dfrac{8}{125}\right)^{-\frac{2}{3}} = \dfrac{25}{4}$

6 The gradient of a curve is given by the formula below:

gradient $= 4x^{\frac{3}{2}} - \dfrac{96}{x^{\frac{5}{2}}}$

Find the value of the gradient when $x = 4$.

16

1 Solve

a $3^x = 81$

b $7^x = 1$

c $8^x = \dfrac{1}{64}$

d $2^x = \dfrac{1}{4}$

e $2^x = \dfrac{1}{128}$

f $10^x = 0.0001$

g $5^x = 0.2$

h $5^x = \dfrac{1}{125}$

i $2^x = 0.125$

2 Copy and complete:

a $16^x = 2$

$\left(2^{\square}\right)^x = 2$

$2^{\square} = 2^1$

$\boxed{} = 1$

$x = \boxed{}$

b $\left(\dfrac{1}{3}\right)^{\frac{x}{3}} = 27$

$\left(3^{\square}\right)^{\frac{x}{3}} = 3^{\square}$

$-\dfrac{x}{3} = \boxed{}$

$x = \boxed{}$

3 Solve

a $16^x = 4$

b $125^x = 25$

c $16^x = 32$

d $13^x = \dfrac{1}{169}$

e $49^x = \dfrac{1}{7}$

f $27^x = \dfrac{1}{9}$

g $8^x = \dfrac{1}{16}$

h $7^x = 49 \times \sqrt{7}$

i $2^x = \dfrac{4}{\sqrt{2}}$

4 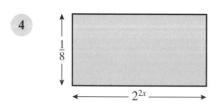 The areas of each rectangle are equal (all lengths are in cm). Find the value of x.

5 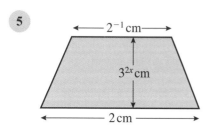 The area of this trapezium is $\dfrac{15}{4}$ cm². Find the value of x.

6 Solve

a $8^{4x} = \dfrac{1}{16}$

b $9^{x-2} = \dfrac{1}{27^x}$

c $125^{\frac{x}{2}} = \dfrac{1}{25^{x+1}}$

d $\left(\dfrac{1}{3}\right)^{2x} = \dfrac{1}{27}$

e $16^x = \dfrac{1}{(\sqrt{2})^4}$

7 The volume of the cuboid opposite is $59\,049\,\text{cm}^3$.
Find the value of x.

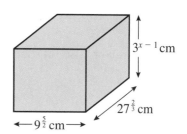

$3^{x-1}\,\text{cm}$

$27^{\frac{2}{3}}\,\text{cm}$

$\longleftarrow 9^{\frac{5}{2}}\,\text{cm} \longrightarrow$

TASK E2.4 ─────────────────────────── **Main Book Page 49**

Do not use a calculator.

1 Which of the following numbers are not square numbers?
   100   110   121   134   139   144   169   180   196   225

2 Between which 2 square numbers do each of the following numbers lie?
   a 181   **b** 40   **c** 200   **d** 75

3 Use your answers from question **2** to estimate each of the following to one decimal place.
   a $\sqrt{181}$ **b** $\sqrt{40}$ **c** $\sqrt{200}$ **d** $\sqrt{75}$

4

$1^3 = 1$	$2^3 = 8$	$3^3 = 27$	$4^3 = 64$
$5^3 = 125$	$6^3 = 216$	$7^3 = 343$	$8^3 = 512$

Use the numbers above to help you estimate each of the following to one decimal place:
   a $\sqrt[3]{200}$ **b** $\sqrt[3]{50}$ **c** $\sqrt[3]{(5^3 + 6^3)}$ **d** $\sqrt[3]{(20^2 - 15^2)}$

5 Estimate $\sqrt[3]{215\,000\,000}$ (consider $\sqrt[3]{215} \times \sqrt[3]{1000} \times \sqrt[3]{1000}$)

6 Estimate $\sqrt{197\,000\,000}$

7 Estimate the answer to each of the following.
   a $\dfrac{3 \cdot 1^3 + \sqrt{120}}{\sqrt{101}}$ **b** $\dfrac{14 \cdot 92^2 - 5 \cdot 03^2}{\sqrt{145} + \sqrt[3]{500}}$ **c** $\dfrac{2 \cdot 01^6 - \sqrt{15 \cdot 97}}{1 \cdot 02^5 + \sqrt{119 \cdot 9}}$

8 If $y = 4x^{\frac{1}{3}}$, estimate the value of y when $x = 217$.

9 If $m = 5(80)^t$, estimate the value of m when $t = \dfrac{1}{2}$.

8 If $p = 8x^t$, estimate the value of p when $x = 2 \cdot 9$ and $t = 4$.

TASK E2.5 ————————————————————

1 Answer true or false for each statement below.

a $5n^{-1} = \dfrac{5}{n}$

b $(x^3)^2 = x^5$

c $\sqrt{(16a^4)} = 4a^4$

d $7^{-2} = \dfrac{2}{7}$

e $\left(\dfrac{4}{9}\right)^{-\frac{1}{2}} = \dfrac{3}{2}$

f $\dfrac{(x^4)^2 \times x^3}{x^7 \times x^4} = 1$

2 *Evaluate* without using a calculator:

a 3^{-2}

b $64^{-\frac{1}{3}}$

c $\left(\dfrac{1}{5}\right)^0$

d $\left(\dfrac{2}{7}\right)^{-1}$

e $16^{\frac{3}{2}}$

f $\left(\dfrac{4}{9}\right)^{\frac{1}{2}}$

g $\left(\dfrac{27}{125}\right)^{\frac{2}{3}}$

h $\left(\dfrac{49}{121}\right)^{-\frac{1}{2}}$

3 Simplify

a $(5a^2)^3$

b $\sqrt{(9m^6n^4)}$

c $(64x^{15})^{\frac{1}{3}}$

4 The area of this rectangle is $27\,\text{cm}^2$
(all lengths are in cm). Find the value of x.

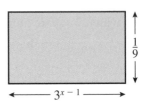

$\dfrac{1}{9}$

3^{x-1}

5 Estimate the difference between $\sqrt[3]{218{\cdot}6}$ and $\sqrt{24{\cdot}73}$.

6 Simplify

a $\dfrac{(4a^3b^4) \times (10a^2b^5)}{5a^4b^2}$

b $\dfrac{(6mn^2) \times (10m^3n^4)}{4mn^2}$

c $\left(5a^{\frac{1}{4}}\right)^2$

7 Express $\dfrac{128 \times 32^4}{64^3}$ as a power of 2.

8 Solve

a $8^x = 2$

b $8^x = 4$

c $25^x = \dfrac{1}{5}$

d $64^x = \dfrac{1}{16}$

e $4^{x+1} = \dfrac{1}{8^{2x}}$

f $27^{2x} = 81^{x-1}$

9 Find x if $\dfrac{4^x \times 16^2}{32^5} = 8$

10

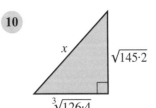

x

$\sqrt{145{\cdot}2}$

$\sqrt[3]{126{\cdot}4}$

Estimate the value of x.
A ... s are in cm.

GEOMETRY 1

3

Find the angles marked with letters.

1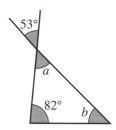

2

3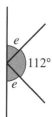

4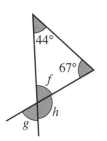

5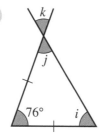

6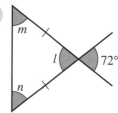

7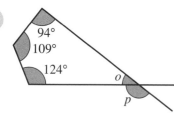

8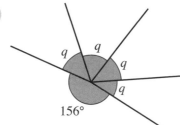

9   **a** Write down the value of AD̂B.
   b Give a reason for your answer.
   c Find the value of CB̂D.
   d Give full reasons for your answer.

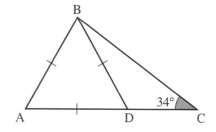

10   **a** Find the value of QP̂R.
   b Give full reasons for your answer.

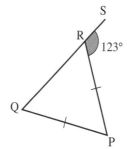

TASK M3.2 ———————————————————— **Main Book Page 64**

Find the angles marked with letters.

1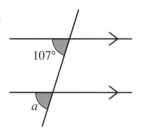

2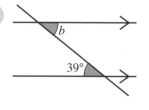

3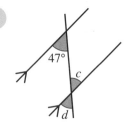

4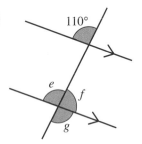

5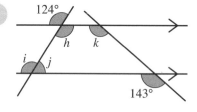

6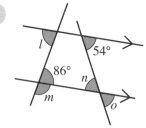

7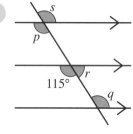

8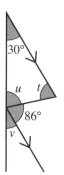

9 **a** Find the value of AB̂E.

　　b Give full reasons for your answer.

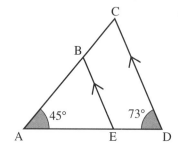

10 **a** Find the value of SQ̂R.

　　b Give full reasons for your answer.

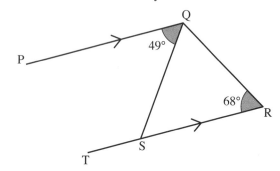

11 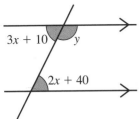   Work out the values of x and y.

$3x + 10$ y

$2x + 40$

12 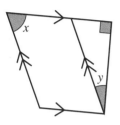   Express y in terms of x.

x

y

TASK M3.3 ——————————————————————— **Main Book Page 66**

1 Copy and complete below.
A pentagon can be split into _ _ _ _ triangles.
Sum of interior angles = _ _ _ _ × 180°
= _ _ _ _ °

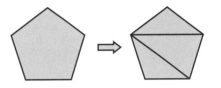

2 Find the sum of the interior angles of an octagon.

3 Find the sum of the interior angles of a polygon with 15 sides.

4 Copy and complete below.
This polygon can be split into _ _ _ _ triangles.
Sum of interior angles = _ _ _ _ × 180° = _ _ _ _ °
Add up all the given angles:
126° + 143° + 109° + 94° + 165° = _ _ _ _ °
angle x = _ _ _ _ °

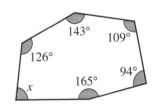

In the questions below, find the angles marked with letters.

5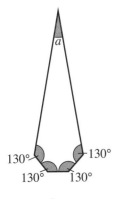

a

130°   130°
130°   130°

6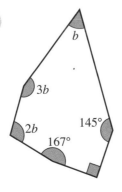

b

$3b$

$2b$ 145°
167°

7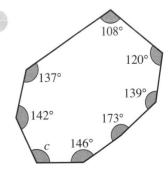

108°
120°
137°
139°
142°   173°
c 146°

22

8 Nine of the ten interior angles of a decagon each equal 145°.
Find the size of the other interior angle.

9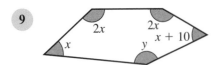
Express y in terms of x.

TASK M3.4 ──────────────────────────────── **Main Book Page 68**

1 An octagon has 8 sides. Find the size of each exterior angle of a *regular* octagon.

2 A decagon has 10 sides.
  a Find the size of each exterior angle of a *regular* decagon.
  b Find the size of each interior angle of a *regular* decagon.

3 Find the size of angle a.

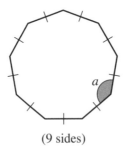

(9 sides)

4 Find the exterior angles of *regular* polygons with
  a 18 sides   **b** 24 sides   **c** 45 sides

5 Find the interior angle of each polygon in question **4**.

6 The exterior angle of a *regular* polygon is 24°.
How many sides has the polygon?

7 The interior angle of a *regular* polygon is 162°.
How many sides has the polygon?

8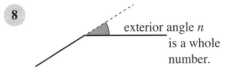
exterior angle n
is a whole
number.

Explain clearly what must be true
about angle n if the polygon is *regular*.

9 In a *regular* polygon, each exterior angle is 140° less than each interior angle.
How many sides has the polygon?

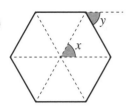

a Calculate angles x and y in the regular hexagon shown opposite.

b Is this relationship true for the equivalent angles in any n-sided regular polygon? Explain your answer fully.

11 All the angles in a polygon are measured as 156°, 145°, 135°, 82°, 165°, 75°, 152° and 178°. The last angle is measured incorrectly. By how many degrees is it in error?

12 Part of a *regular* dodecagon (12 sides) is shown.
O is the centre of the polygon.
Find the value of x.

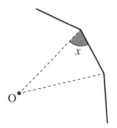

| **TASK M3.5** | **Main Book Page 71** |

1 Prove that the sum of the angles in a quadrilateral add up to 360°.
Give all your reasons clearly.

2 Prove that triangle QUT is isosceles.
Give all your reasons clearly.

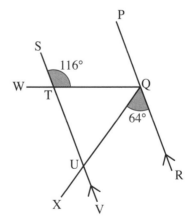

3

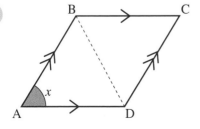

ABCD is a rhombus.

Prove that $B\hat{D}C = 90° - \dfrac{1}{2}x$

24

4 P   Q   R   Express angle PSQ in terms of x.

S

5 ABCD is a rectangle. Prove that triangle
ABM is isosceles.
Give all your reasons clearly.

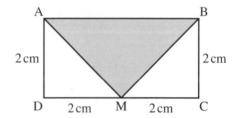

6 Prove that $A\hat{D}C = B\hat{A}C$.
Give all your reasons clearly.

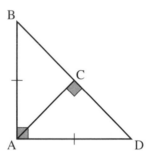

7 Prove that the opposite angles in a rhombus are equal.

8 Express $B\hat{C}D$ in terms of x.

B

A   C   D

TASK E3.1 ——————————————————————— **Main Book Page 74**

Find the angles marked with letters. (O is the centre of each circle)

1

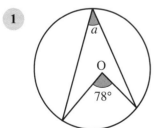

2

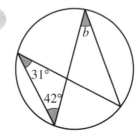

3

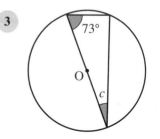

4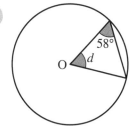

5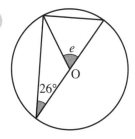

6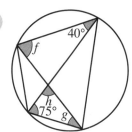

7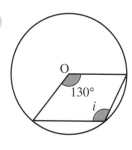

8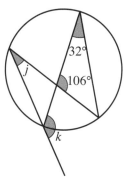

9 In this question, write down *all the reasons* for your answers.
Find

  a OÊG

  b OĜF

  c OF̂G

  d FÊO

  e EF̂G

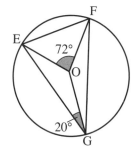

10 Find BĈD.
Write down *the reasons* for your answer.

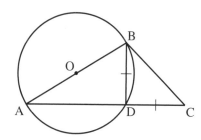

11 Find *x*

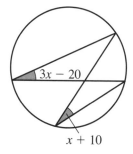

12 Find *y*

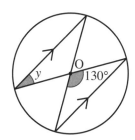

13

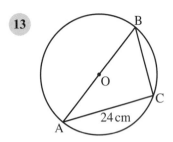

The radius of the circle opposite is 12·5 cm.
Work out the length of BC.
Explain your method fully.

14

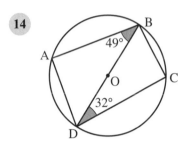

The diameter of the circle opposite is 10 cm.
Work out the perimeter of the quadrilateral ABCD.
Give the answer to one decimal place.

TASK E3.2 ———————————————————— **Main Book Page 77**

Find the angles marked with letters. (O is the centre of each circle)

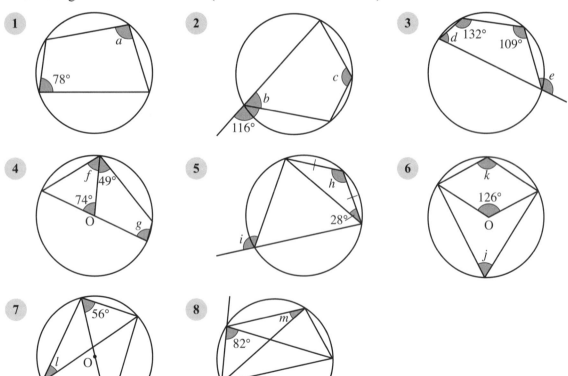

9 In this question, write down *all the reasons* for your answers.

Find

a QR̂S

b QÔS

c SQ̂O

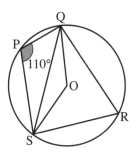

10 In this question, write down *all the reasons* for your answers.

Find

a CD̂O

b CÔD

c AB̂C

d AÔC

e AÔD

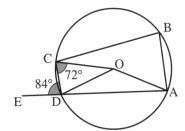

11 Find x

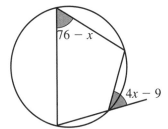

12 Find y

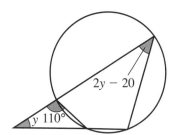

| **TASK E3.3** | **Main Book Page 79** |

Find the angles marked with letters. (O is the centre of each circle)

1

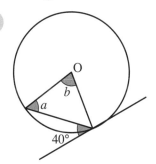

2

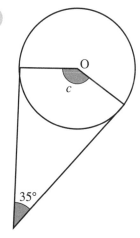

3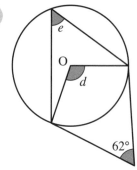

4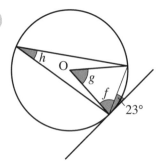

5 In this question, write down *all the reasons* for your answers.
Find

a BÔC

b BD̂C

c CÂB

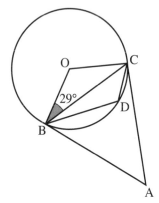

6 In this question, write down *all the reasons* for your answers.
Find

a PÔR

b PQ̂O

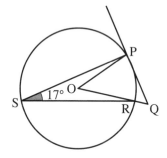

7 Find x

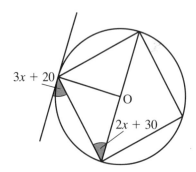

8 In each part of the question below, find x giving each answer to one decimal place.

a

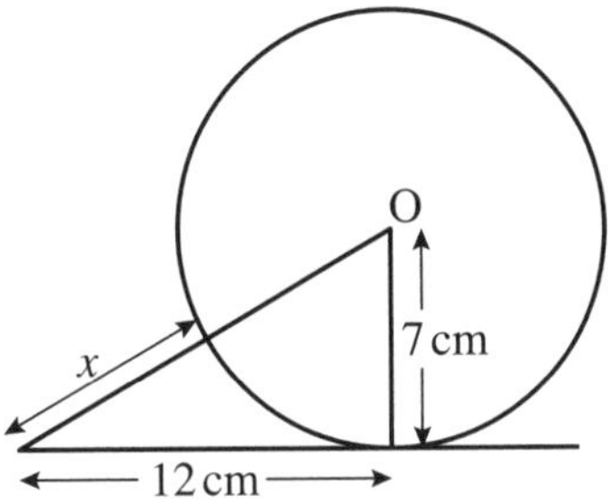

O

7 cm

x

12 cm

b

O

5 cm

x

14 cm

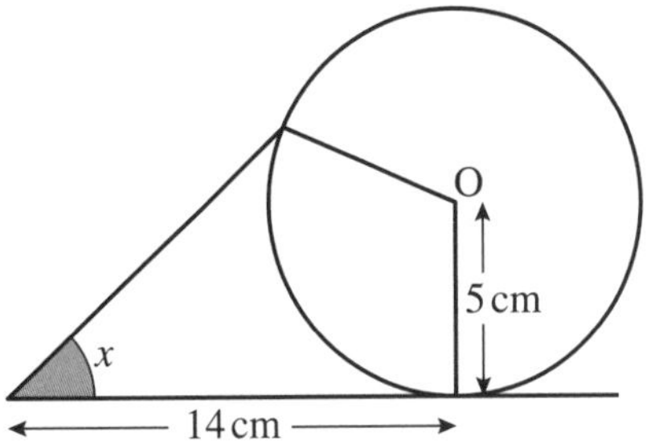

TASK E3.4 ──────────────────── **Main Book Page 82**

Find the angles marked with letters. (O is the centre of each circle)

1

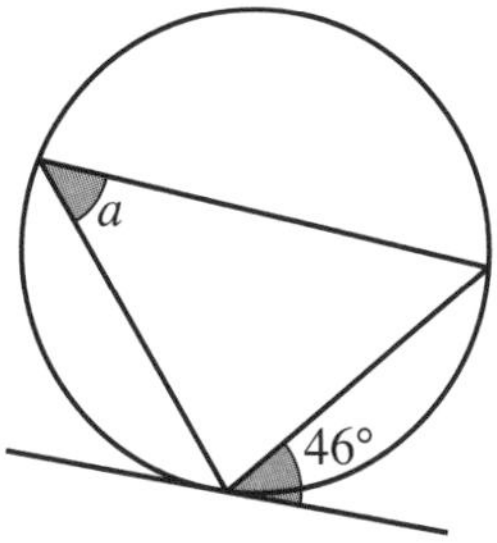

a

46°

2

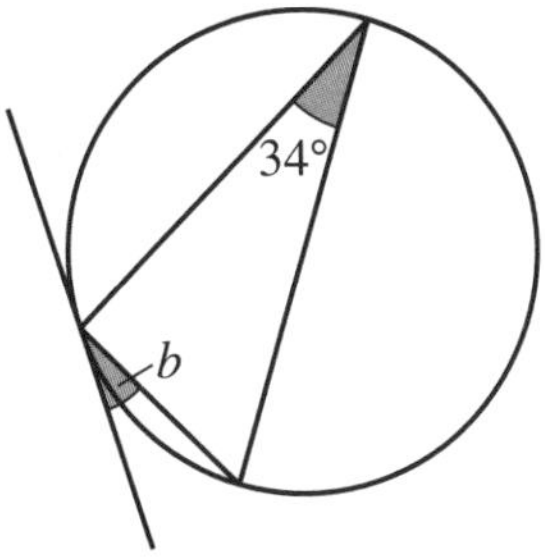

34°

b

3

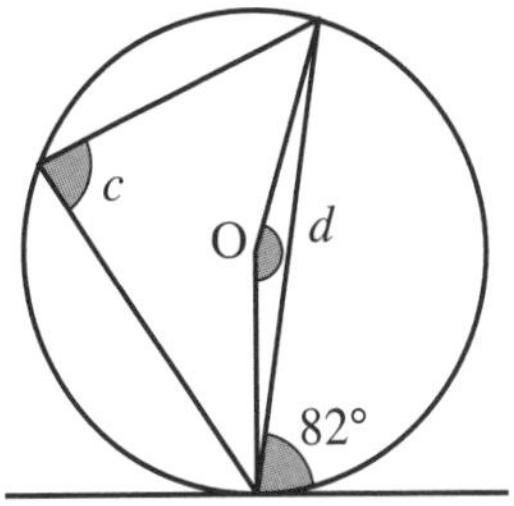

c

O d

82°

4

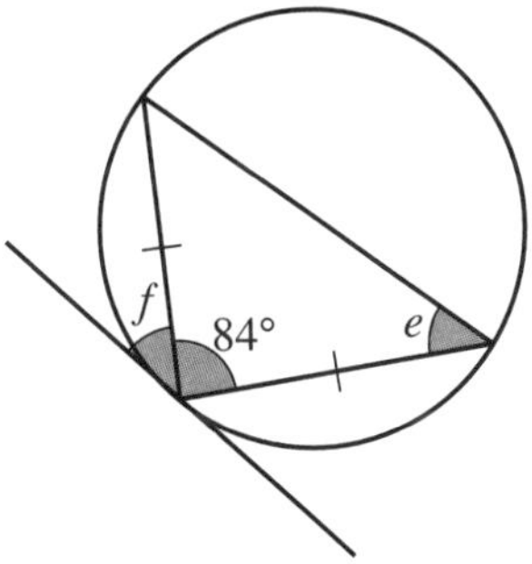

f 84° e

5

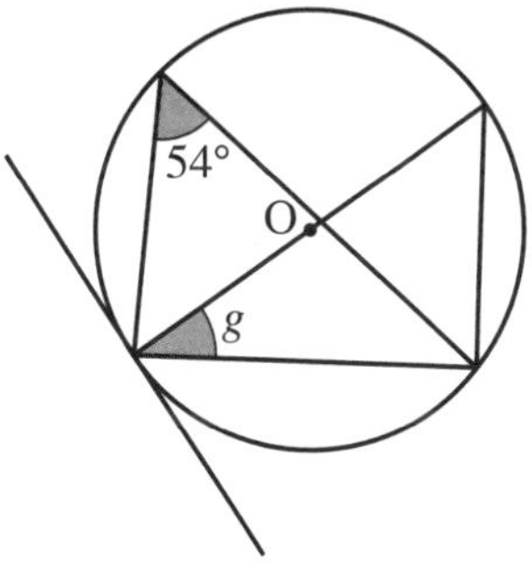

54°

O

g

6

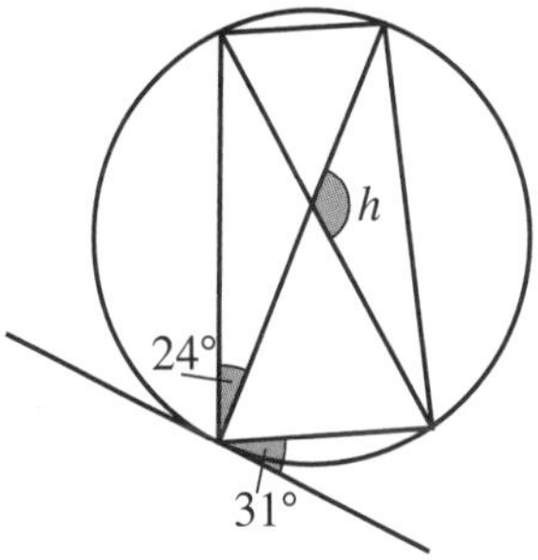

h

24°

31°

7

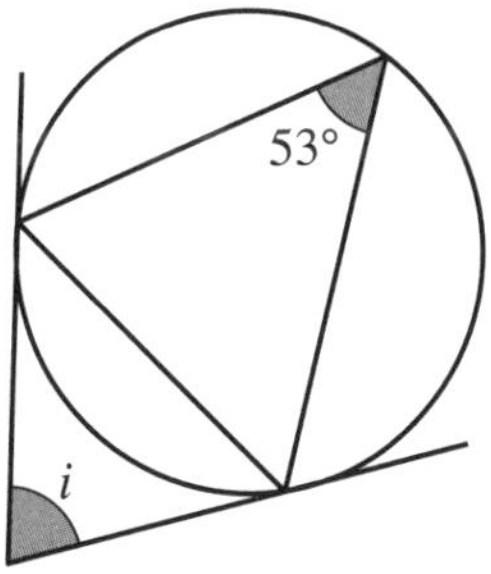

53°

i

8

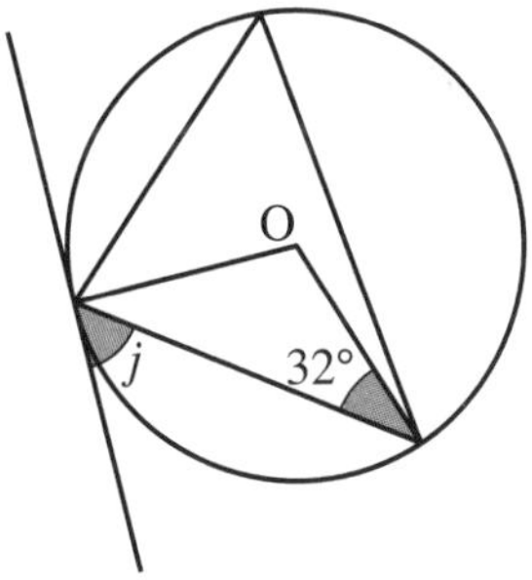

O

j 32°

9 In this question, write down *all the reasons*
for your answers.
Find

   a PQ̂S

   b SÛQ

   c SÔQ

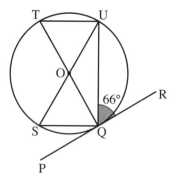

10 In this question, write down *all the reasons*
for your answers.
Find

   a BD̂G

   b AB̂G

   c DB̂F

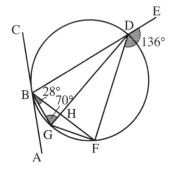

11 Find *x*

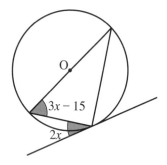

12 Find *x* and *y*

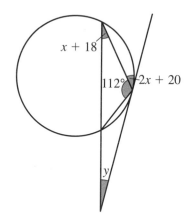

13 In the diagram opposite,
AB = BE.

Express AB̂E in
terms of *x*.
Give reasons for
your answer.

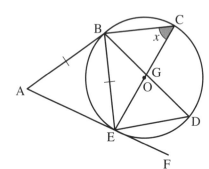

Main Book Page 85

1 Prove that $P\hat{S}T = x$ (ie. the exterior angle of a cyclic quadrilateral equals the opposite interior angle).

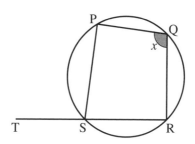

2 O is the centre of the circle. Copy and complete the statements below to prove that 'the angle at the centre of a circle is twice the angle at the circumference.'

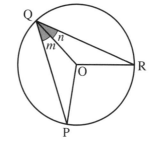

$O\hat{P}Q = \square$ (triangle OPQ is isosceles)

$P\hat{O}Q = \square$ (sum of angles in a triangle $= 180°$)

$O\hat{R}Q = \square$ (triangle ORQ is isosceles)

$R\hat{O}Q = \square$ (sum of angles in a triangle $= 180°$)

$P\hat{O}R = 360 - P\hat{O}Q - R\hat{O}Q$ (sum of angles at a point add up to $360°$)

$P\hat{O}R = 360 - (\square) - (\square)$

$\quad = 360 - \square + \square - \square + \square$

$\quad = \square + \square$

$\quad = 2(\square + \square)$

This proves that $P\hat{O}R = 2 \times P\hat{Q}R$, ie. the angle at the centre of the circle is twice the angle at the circumference.

3 O is the centre of the circle. Find the following angles in terms of x and y, *giving all your reasons*.

  a $D\hat{B}E$

  b $D\hat{F}E$

  c $G\hat{F}D$

  d $D\hat{O}E$

  e $O\hat{E}D$

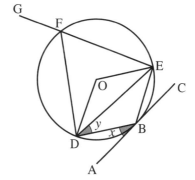

4 Prove the alternate segment theorem.

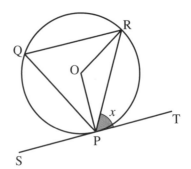

5 US is a tangent to the circle.
Express y in terms of x.

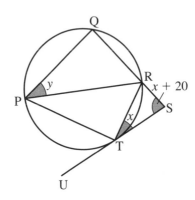

ALGEBRA 1   4

TASK M4.1 ——————————————————— **Main Book Page 97**

In questions **1** to **20** find the value of each expression

when $f = -1$
$\qquad g = 5$
$\qquad h = -4$

1 $\dfrac{1}{2}h$ **2** $3f$ **3** fg **4** $\dfrac{3}{4}fh$ **5** $2g - \dfrac{1}{4}h$

6 $3f + 4g$ **7** $4f + 3g$ **8** h^2 **9** $g^2 + h^2$ **10** $16 - h$

11 $f + g + h$ **12** $\dfrac{2}{5}g + 6f$ **13** $6h + 10$ **14** $3(f + g)$ **15** $7(g - f)$

16 $(4f)^2$ **17** $4g - 3f + 3h$ **18** $\dfrac{6h}{2f}$ **19** $\dfrac{7(f + g)}{h}$ **20** $2h^2$

In questions **21** to **40** find the value of each expression

when $a = -2$
$b = -5$
$c = 3$

21 $a^2(c - b)$

22 $\dfrac{3}{4}a^2$

23 $(2b)^2 - 3b^2$

24 $(4c)^2 + (5a)^2$

25 $\dfrac{4}{5}b^3$

26 $a(bc - a^2)$

27 $\dfrac{2b + 4a}{3c}$

28 $\dfrac{3}{25}a^2b^2$

29 $b^2 + 6ab$

30 $\dfrac{4c - 9a}{2b}$

31 $a^2 + ac - b$

32 $\dfrac{4b}{a} - \dfrac{10c}{b}$

33 $\dfrac{b(c^2 - a)}{a - c}$

34 $a^3 + c^3$

35 $(a - 2b)(2c - b)$

36 $2c^3 - 2b^2$

37 $(a^2 - b)(a^2 + b)$

38 $\dfrac{1}{10}abc$

39 $\dfrac{4}{5}a^2bc$

40 $\dfrac{b^2 + 5a^2}{c^2}$

TASK M4.2 ——————————————— **Main Book Page 98**

1 The total surface area A of this cuboid is given by the formula
$A = 2lw + 2lh + 2hw$
Find the value of A when
a $l = 5$, $w = 3$ and $h = 1$
b $l = 10$, $w = 2{\cdot}5$ and $h = 4$

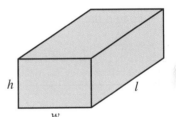

2 The total surface area A of a sphere is given by the formula
$A = 12r^2$
Find the value of A when
a $r = 3$ **b** $r = 5$ **c** $r = 8$

3 Energy E is given by the formula $E = mc^2$ where m is the mass and c is the speed of light. Find the value of E when $m = 15$ and $c = 3{,}00\,000\,000$.

4 The formula $s = ut + \dfrac{1}{2}at^2$ gives the displacement s of a particle after time t.
The acceleration is a and the initial velocity is u.
Find s (to 3 significant figures if necessary) when
a $u = 3$, $t = 12$ and $a = 6{\cdot}4$
b $u = -8{\cdot}17$, $a = -9{\cdot}81$, $t = 4{\cdot}5$

34

5 The area A of a trapezium is given by the formula

$A = \frac{1}{2}h(a + b)$

Find the value of A when

a $a = 6, b = 13, h = 12$ **b** $h = 3.26, a = 4.9, b = 7.48$

6 The length of the diagonal AB is given by the formula

$AB = \sqrt{(x^2 + y^2 + z^2)}$

Find the value of AB when $x = 13\,cm$, $y = 8\,cm$ and $z = 5\,cm$. (give your answer to one decimal place)

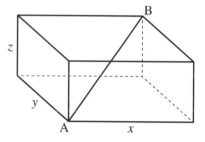

7 The mass m of a radioactive substance present at time t is given by the formula

$m = 100(2^{-t})$

Find the value of m when

a $t = 0$ **b** $t = 1$ **c** $t = 4$

8 If $\frac{1}{f} = \frac{1}{u} + \frac{1}{v}$, find the value of f when $u = 8$ and $v = 17$.

TASK M4.3 ———————————————————— **Main Book Page 100**

In questions **1** to **6** answer true or false.

1 $a + a = a^2$ **2** $5m + m = 6m$ **3** $6n^2 - n^2 = 6$

4 $4y \times y = 4y^2$ **5** $a \times 5 \times b = 5ab$ **6** $16x \div 4 = 12x$

Simplify

7 $4a \times -6b$ **8** $-3m \times -2p$ **9** $-15x \div 5$

10 $-3p \times 7q$ **11** $-a \times 3a$ **12** $-42a^2 \div -2$

Multiply out

13 $2(3y + 5)$ **14** $6(2a - b)$ **15** $7(2x + 5)$

16 $x(x - y)$ **17** $m(m - 3p)$ **18** $c(2d + 1)$

Write down and *simplify* an expression for the area of each shape below:

19 $2a + b$ | 5

20 $4b - 1$ | a

21 $m + 8p$ | m

22 Lily expands $6(4n - 3)$ and writes down $24n - 3$.
Explain clearly what mistake Lily has made.

Expand

23 $-5(x - 3)$

24 $-2(3m - 4)$

25 $-m(2 - p)$

26 $-y(x + z)$

27 $-x(x + 3y)$

28 $-(a - b)$

29 $-q(q - 8r)$

30 $3a(3a + 4b)$

31 $-8x(4x - 3y)$

32 $-y(y^2 + 3x)$

33 $4n^2(3n - 7)$

34 $5xy(4x + 2y^2)$

35 $6ab(2a - 3b)$

36 $8p^2q(3q - p)$

37 $7m^2n^2(3n + 4mn^2)$

TASK M4.4 | **Main Book Page 101**

Expand and simplify

1 $3(a + 4) + 7$

2 $9(2b + 4) + 4b$

3 $7(5a + 6) - 10a$

Simplify

4 $3(8y + 6) + 2(2y - 5)$

5 $5n + 9 + 6(2n + 3)$

6 $4b + 9(3b + 6) - 24$

7 $7(4c + 7) + 3(2c - 8)$

8

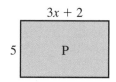

$3x + 2$ | 5 | P

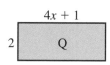

$4x + 1$ | 2 | Q

Six rectangles with the dimensions of rectangle P are joined to 5 rectangles with the dimensions of rectangle Q. Write down and simplify an expression for the total area of the combined rectangles.

Copy and complete

9 $6(3a + 2) - 4(2a + 2) = \boxed{} + 12 - \boxed{} - 8 = \boxed{} + 4$

10 $7(4x + 3) - 5(3x - 6) = 28x + \boxed{} - 15x + \boxed{} = 13x + \boxed{}$

Expand and simplify

11 $5(a + 4) - 3(a + 2)$

12 $6(2m + 3) - 5(m + 3)$

13 $4(5y + 6) - 2(4y + 3)$

14 $2(8b + 9) - 4(4b - 6)$

15 $8a - 3(2a - 5) + 6$

16 $7x - 4(x - 1) - 3$

17 $9(4n + 7) - 5(2n + 4)$

18 $10q + 3(5 - 2q) + 4(7q + 4)$

19 $3x(2x + 3) + 5x(x - 2)$

20 $5n(3n^2 - 4) - 2n(4n^2 + 5)$

21 $4m(2m - n) - 3n(4m + n)$

22 $3a(4a + 2b - 3c) - 4b(5a - 2c)$

TASK M4.5   **Main Book Page 103**

Multiply out

1 $(x + 3)(x + 2)$

2 $(m + 4)(m + 7)$

3 $(c - 4)(c - 2)$

4 $(y - 8)(y + 2)$

5 $(y - 7)(y + 3)$

6 $(n - 9)(n - 4)$

7 Explain why $(x + 6)^2$ is *not* equal to $x^2 + 36$.

Expand

8 $(n + 7)^2$

9 $(y - 4)^2$

10 $(x - 8)^2$

11 Louis says that the area of each shape shown opposite is equal. Show clearly whether he is correct or not.

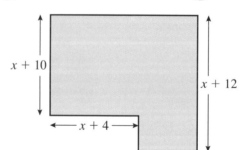
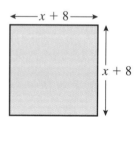

Multiply out

12 $(3x + 2)(5x + 4)$

13 $(5a + 4)(2a + 1)$

14 $(2n - 4)(3n + 7)$

15 $(7y - 6)(3y - 2)$

16 $(4a + 6)^2$

17 $(5m - 9)^2$

18 $(6 + 5y)(6 + y)$ **19** $(9 - 4c)(7 + 2c)$ **20** $(4x - 2y)(8x + 3y)$

Expand and simplify

21 $(m + 4)^2 + (m + 7)^2$ **22** $(c + 6)^2 - (c - 1)^2$ **23** $(2x^4 + 5y^6)^2$

24 $(5a^2 + 3b^3)(2a^2 + 5b^3) - (3a^2 + 4b^3)^2$

| TASK M4.6 | Main Book Page 105 |

1 Show that $(x + 4)^2 \equiv x^2 + 8x + 16$
For how many different values of x is this true?

2 Expand and simplify $3(x^2 + 5x) + 2(3x - 1)$
How many terms does the final simplified expression contain?

3 Polly says that $5x^2 - 4x + 1$ is an expression. Gavin disagrees. Explain who is correct.

4
$\boxed{4x + 1 > 9}$ $\boxed{7x^2 - x = 3}$

$\boxed{4x - 3}$ $\boxed{2(3x + 1) \equiv 6x + 2}$

$\boxed{6xy + y - 3}$ $\boxed{5x^2 + 4x - 3}$

$\boxed{5x + 4 = 9}$ $\boxed{8x^3 = 12}$

    a Write down the equations shown opposite.

    b Write down the expressions shown opposite.

5 Ishaan says that $(x + 4)(x - 4)$ is equal to $(x^2 - 16)$. Natalie says that $(x + 4)(x - 4)$ is identical to $(x^2 - 16)$. Strictly speaking, who is correct and why?

6 How many values of x will satisfy $x^2 - 3x = 4$? Does this mean it is an equation or an identity?

7
$\boxed{x^2 - 3xy + xy - y + 4x^2}$ $\boxed{5xy + 10x^2 - xy^2 + 5x^2 + 3y}$

Simplify the expressions above and write down the expression which has more terms.

8 $8x + 4 = 3x + 5$ *Explain* why this is an equation and not an identity.

| TASK E4.1 | Main Book Page 106 |

1 Find the volume of this cuboid, simplifying your answer as far as possible.

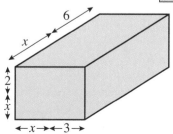

Expand, giving each answer in its simplest form.

2 $(x + 5)(x + 3)(x + 6)$

3 $(x - 2)(x + 3)(x - 4)$

4 $(x + 3)^3$

5 $(x - 4)^3$

6 $(x - 4)^2(x + 1)$

7 $(3x + 1)(2x + 3)(5x + 1)$

8 $(2x + 3)(2x - 3)(x + 5)$

9 $(x + 2)^3 - (x + 1)^3$

10 $(x + 2)$ members of a theatre club each pay £$(x - 3)$ to watch a show. During one year they each watch $(x + 2)$ shows. Write down a simplified expression for the total amount of money spent on the shows.

| **TASK M4.7** | **Main Book Page 108** |

Copy and complete

1 $n^2 + 7n = n\left(n + \boxed{}\right)$

2 $4mp - 10m = 2m\left(2p - \boxed{}\right)$

3 $4ab + 18bc = 2b\left(\boxed{} + \boxed{}\right)$

4 $x^2y - 3xy^2 = xy\left(\boxed{} - \boxed{}\right)$

Factorise these expressions completely

5 $xy + yz$

6 $a^2 - 6a$

7 $m^2 + 2p$

8 $c^2 + 9c$

9 $mp - pq$

10 $3xy + 9xz$

11 $10ab - 15ac$

12 $18wz - 15wy$

13 $12fg + 21f$

14 $4a^2 - 6a$

15 $5p^2 - 30pq$

16 $18mp + 30m$

17 $8pq - 20q^2$

18 $16xyz - 28y^2$

19 $33a^2 + 55abc$

Factorise completely

20 $12m^2n - 9mn^2$

21 $25a^2b + 15abc$

22 $6x^2y + 15x^3$

23 $21m^3 - 28mn^2$

24 $48pq^2r - 36p^2qr$

25 $8xy^2 + 20xyz + 6yz^2$

26 $40a^3b - 56ab^2 + 32a^2b^3$

27 $36m^2n^3p^2 - 54mn^3p^3 - 27m^2n^2p^2$

Prove that

28 $5(2x + 5) + 7 = 2(5x + 16)$

29 $3(6x + 7) + 11 - 2(4x + 1) = 10(x + 3)$

TASK M4.8 ──────────────────────────── **Main Book Page 109**

Factorise the following

1 $x^2 + 12x + 35$ **2** $m^2 + 12m + 27$ **3** $y^2 - 4y + 3$

4 $n^2 - 2n - 24$ **5** $a^2 - 6a - 27$ **6** $c^2 - 8c - 20$

7 $n^2 - 11n + 24$ **8** $y^2 - 14y + 45$ **9** $a^2 + a - 30$

10 $x^2 - x - 72$ **11** $p^2 + 15p + 44$ **12** $m^2 + 4m - 60$

13 $a^2 - 15a + 56$ **14** $q^2 + 4q - 96$ **15** $b^2 - 5b - 150$

16 Write $x^2 + 2x + 1$ in the form $(x + a)^2$. Write down the value of a.

17 Write $x^2 + 8x + 16$ in the form $(x + b)^2$. Write down the value of b.

18 Write $x^2 - 6x + 9$ in the form $(x - c)^2$. Write down the value of c.

19 Write $x^2 - 14x + 49$ in the form $(x - d)^2$. Write down the value of d.

Collect like terms then factorise:

20 $3x^2 + 9x - 2(2x + 1) - 2x^2 + 8$ **21** $x(x + 3) + 3 - x(x + 5) + x(x - 2) - 15$

22 The total area of the shape opposite is
$2x^2 - 10x + 29$
Find an expression for y in terms of x.

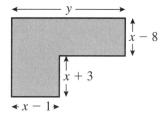

23 The area of rectangle ABCD is $x^2 - 2x - 24$.
Alex says that an expression for the length
of AB is $(x - 4)$. *Explain* clearly whether
Alex is correct or not.

TASK M4.9 ──────────────────────────── **Main Book Page 110**

Factorise

1 $x^2 - y^2$ **2** $b^2 - 3^2$ **3** $y^2 - 5^2$ **4** $a^2 - 64$

5 $n^2 - 4$ **6** $p^2 - 1$ **7** $36 - x^2$ **8** $9y^2 - z^2$

9 $49 - 4a^2$ **10** $49x^2 - 81y^2$ **11** $144m^2 - 25$ **12** $16b^2 - \dfrac{1}{9}$

40

Copy and complete

13 $5x^2 - 20$

$= \boxed{}(x^2 - 4)$

$= \boxed{}\left(x + \boxed{}\right)\left(x - \boxed{}\right)$

14 $12a^2 - 27b^2$

$= 3\left(\boxed{} - \boxed{}\right)$

$= 3\left(\boxed{} + \boxed{}\right)\left(\boxed{} - \boxed{}\right)$

15 $4m^2 - 8m - 60$

$= 4\left(m^2 - \boxed{} - \boxed{}\right)$

$= 4\left(m + \boxed{}\right)\left(m - \boxed{}\right)$

Factorise completely

16 $3n^2 - 48$

17 $50 - 2b^2$

18 $5t^2 + 15t + 10$

19 $6n^2 - 42n + 60$

20 $12p^2 - 147$

21 $4x^2 - 16x - 48$

22 $7y^2 + 42y - 49$

23 $80 - 45a^2$

24 $32x^2 - 162y^2$

25 $9a^2 - 9a - 180$

26 $10m^2 - 80m + 160$

27 $72y^2 - 338$

28 $9\pi^2 - 1$

29 $\frac{1}{4}e^2 - 25$

30 $(4x^3 + 3)^2 - (4x^3 - 3)^2$

31 $(5x^2 - 6)^2 - (5x^2 + 6)^2$

32 $e^2 - 16\pi^2$

33 $(3x + \sqrt{5})^2 - (3x - \sqrt{5})^2$

34 Use the difference of 2 squares to evaluate $15 \cdot 7^2 - 4 \cdot 3^2$ without using a calculator.

Factorise completely

35 $x^3 - 10x^2 + 21x$

36 $x^4 + 2x^2 + 1$

37 $x^4 - 3x^2 - 18$

TASK E4.2 | **Main Book Page 112**

Copy and complete

1 $mp + mq - np - nq$

$= m\left(\boxed{} + \boxed{}\right) - n\left(\boxed{} + \boxed{}\right)$

$= \left(\boxed{} + \boxed{}\right)(m - n)$

2 $a^2 - ac - ab + bc$

$= a\left(\boxed{} - \boxed{}\right) - b\left(\boxed{} - \boxed{}\right)$

$= \left(\boxed{} - \boxed{}\right)(a - b)$

Factorise

3 $mx + nx + my + ny$

4 $ac - bc - ad + bd$

5 $pr + ps - qr - qs$

6 $p^2 + pr - pq - qr$

7 $m^2 - mn - mk + kn$

8 $ab - 3c + 3b - ac$

9 $8ac + 10ad + 4bc + 5bd$

10 $20x^2 - 15xy + 16xz - 12yz$

11 $e\theta + 3\mu e - 2\pi\theta - 6\pi\mu$

12 $\sin\theta \sin\alpha + \cos\theta \sin\alpha - \sin\theta \cos\alpha - \cos\theta \cos\alpha$

Copy and complete

1 $5x^2 + 13x - 6$

$= 5x^2 + 15x - \boxed{} - 6$

$= 5x\left(\boxed{} + \boxed{}\right) - 2\left(\boxed{} + \boxed{}\right)$

$= \left(\boxed{} + \boxed{}\right)(5x - 2)$

2 $6x^2 - 19x + 10$

$= 6x^2 - 15x - \boxed{} + 10$

$= 3x\left(\boxed{} - \boxed{}\right) - \boxed{}\left(\boxed{} - \boxed{}\right)$

$= \left(\boxed{} - \boxed{}\right)\left(3x - \boxed{}\right)$

Factorise each expression below

3 $5x^2 + 21x + 4$

4 $3a^2 + 20a + 12$

5 $10y^2 - 17y + 3$

6 $6n^2 - 13n - 5$

7 $14c^2 + 15c - 9$

8 $4x^2 - 81$

9 $20m^2 - 31m + 12$

10 $36a^2 + 19a - 6$

11 $200n^2 + 30n + 1$

12 $18p^2 - 25p - 3$

13 $100x^2 + 44x - 3$

14 $35m^2 - 69m + 28$

15 The area of a rectangle is $(15x^2 + 14x + 3)\,\text{cm}^2$. Work out an expression for the perimeter of the rectangle.

16 Grace factorises $10x^2 + 16x - 8$ and writes down the answer $(2x + 4)(5x - 2)$. Josh says she has not factorised the expression *completely*. Explain clearly why Josh believes this is the case.

Copy and complete

1 $x^2 - 3x - 18 = 0$

$(x - 6)\left(x + \boxed{}\right) = 0$

$x - 6 = 0 \text{ or } x + \boxed{} = 0$

$x = \boxed{} \text{ or } x = \boxed{}$

2 $n^2 + 3n = 0$

$n\left(\boxed{} + \boxed{}\right) = 0$

$n = 0 \text{ or } \boxed{} + \boxed{} = 0$

$n = 0 \text{ or } n = \boxed{}$

3 $a^2 - 4a = 5$

$a^2 - 4a - \boxed{} = 0$

$(a + 1)\left(a - \boxed{}\right) = 0$

$a + 1 = 0 \text{ or } a - \boxed{} = 0$

$a = \boxed{} \text{ or } a = \boxed{}$

Solve these equations

4 $x^2 - 3x + 2 = 0$

5 $a^2 + 4a + 3 = 0$

6 $m^2 + 7m + 10 = 0$

7 $y^2 + y - 12 = 0$

8 $n^2 + 3n - 10 = 0$

9 $x^2 - 8x + 12 = 0$

10 $c^2 + 2c - 15 = 0$

11 $(m - 6)(m + 4) = 0$

12 $(a - 3)(a - 7) = 0$

13 $n^2 - 5n = 0$

14 $x^2 + 7x = 0$

15 $y^2 = 6y$

16 $p^2 + 5p = 14$

17 $n^2 + 32 = 12n$

18 $b^2 - 3b = 0$

19 $x^2 - 13x + 30 = 0$

20 $a^2 + 36 = 13a$

21 $m(m + 2) = 24 - 3m$

22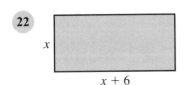

The area of this rectangle is 91 cm².
Form an equation involving x then solve
it to find the value of x.

TASK E4.4 ────────────────────────────── **Main Book Page 116**

Solve the following equations

1 $3p^2 - 11p + 6 = 0$

2 $10a^2 - 3a - 1 = 0$

3 $8y^2 + 10y + 3 = 0$

4 $21m^2 - 41m + 10 = 0$

5 $4m^2 = m$

6 $4h^2 + 4h - 15 = 0$

7 $(9x - 1)(5x - 1) = 0$

8 $15w^2 - 14w = 8$

9 $4y^2 - 25 = 0$

10 $4h^2 - 12h + 8 = 0$

11 $5n^2 - 14 = 33n$

12 $n^3 - 3n^2 - 10n = 0$

13 $6n + 5 - \dfrac{4}{n} = 0$

14 $15w - \dfrac{12}{w} = 11$

15 $(3x + 2)^2 = (x + 6)^2$

16 Solve   **a** $2x^2 - 13x + 15 = 0$ **b** $2w^4 - 13w^2 + 15 = 0$

17 Solve $m^4 = 13m^2 - 36$

TASK E4.5 ────────────────────────────── **Main Book Page 117**

1 The base of a triangle is 4 cm longer than its height. Let the height of the triangle be x.
   a If the area of the triangle is 30 cm², show that
$$x^2 + 4x - 60 = 0$$
   b Find the base of the triangle.

2 A square piece of paper is trimmed to form a rectangle. One of its sides is reduced by 3 cm and the other is reduced by 4 cm. The resulting rectangle has an area of 20 cm². If the side length of the initial square was s,
   a Write down a quadratic equation involving s
   b Solve this equation to find s

3 A square is adjoined by two rectangles, each of length 5 units. If the total area is then 39 square units, what is the length of the square?

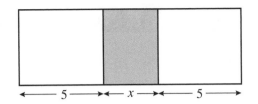

4 A rectangular garden measures 10 m by 15 m. Its width and length are then both increased by x metres. If its area is now 266 m², find x.

5 A small rectangular field is 5 m longer than it is wide. The diagonal of the field is 25 m.

   a If the width of the field is x, show that
$$x^2 + 5x - 300 = 0$$

   b Find the dimensions of the field.

6 Work out the area of triangle ABC.

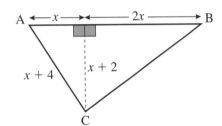

7 Two numbers differ by $\frac{1}{2}$. Their product is 68.

   a If the smaller number is x, show that
$$2x^2 + x - 136 = 0$$

   b Write down the value of each number if they are positive.

8 A pencil box (in the shape of a cuboid) is 9 cm longer than it is wide and 1 cm higher than it is wide. The longest pencil which can be jammed into the case is 13 cm long. Find the dimensions of the pencil case.

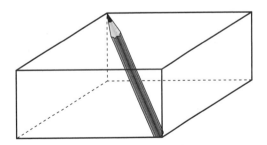

NUMBER 3   5

TASK M5.1/M5.2 —   Main Book Page 127

1   **a** List all the factors of 18.

    b List all the factors of 30.

    c Write down the Highest Common Factor of 18 and 30.

2   Add together all the prime numbers between 20 and 40.

3   Using any method, write the following numbers as products of prime factors, leaving each answer in index form:

    a 75   **b** 44   **c** 80   **d** 594

4 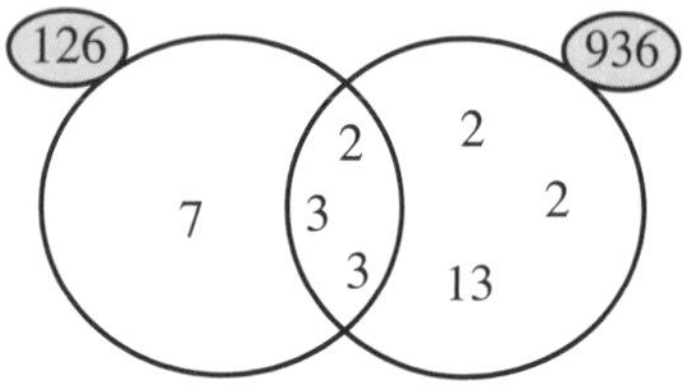   Use this Venn diagram to find

    a the HCF of 126 and 936

    b the LCM of 126 and 936

    (Venn diagram: 126 and 936; left circle contains 7; intersection contains 2, 3, 3; right circle contains 2, 2, 13)

5 $1617 = 3 \times 7 \times 7 \times 11$ and $273 = 3 \times 7 \times 13$

    Find the Highest Common Factor of 273 and 1617.

6 $4mn^2 = 2 \times 2 \times m \times n \times n$ $6m^3n^3 = 2 \times 3 \times m \times m \times m \times n \times n \times n$

    a Find the Highest Common Factor of $4mn^2$ and $6m^3n^3$.

    b Find the Lowest Common Multiple of $4mn^2$ and $6m^3n^3$.

7   Amy and Josh are racing each other. Amy takes 5 minutes to complete one lap. Josh takes 7 minutes to complete one lap. After how many minutes will Amy and Josh pass the starting point at exactly the same time?

8   The Highest Common Factor of two numbers is 8. The Lowest Common Multiple of the same two numbers is 48. Write down the two numbers.

9 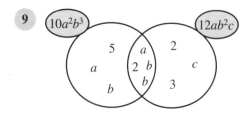 Use this Venn diagram to find the Lowest Common Multiple of $10a^2b^3$ and $12ab^2c$.

10 Find **a** the HCF and **b** the LCM of 396 and 420.

11 Find **a** the HCF and **b** the LCM of 198 and 220.

12 Gill saves £105 each week for x weeks. Matt saves £147 each week for y weeks. If Gill and Matt end up saving the same total amount of money, write down the smallest possible values for x and y.

TASK M5.3 ──────────────────────────────── **Main Book Page 129**

1 Write the numbers below in standard form.

> **Remember:**
> a standard form number will have the form $A \times 10^n$ where $1 \leq A < 10$

    a 3000   **b** 70 000   **c** 340   **d** 89 000

    e 486 000   **f** 598   **g** 9 million   **h** 76 million

2 Remember that $570 = 5.7 \times 10^2$ but $0.057 = 5.7 \times 10^{-2}$.
Write the numbers below in standard form

    a 0.004   **b** 0.0007   **c** 0.9   **d** 0.0018

    e 0.528   **f** 0.000019   **g** 0.0034   **h** 0.00000817

3 Write each number below as an ordinary number.

    a 6×10^4 **b** 3×10^2 **c** 3×10^{-2} **d** 5.6×10^4

    e 2.4×10^5 **f** 8.6×10^{-3} **g** 4.16×10^3 **h** 7.68×10^{-1}

4 $3700 = 37 \times 10^2$. *Explain* why this number is not written in standard form.

5 $28\,000 = 28 \times 10^3$. This number is not written in standard form.
Write it correctly in standard form.

6 Write the numbers below in standard form.

    a 0.0007   **b** 53 000   **c** 0.096   **d** 0.487

    e 49 000 000   **f** 576 000   **g** 0.00074   **h** 82.4

    i 0.1   **j** 0.000000864   **k** 6 180 000   **l** 42 000 000

TASK M5.4 ──────────────────────────────── **Main Book Page 131**

Do not use a calculator.

1 Write each number below in standard form.

    a 73×10^4 **b** 42×10^{14} **c** 0.8×10^7 **d** 0.32×10^{24}

    e 0.68×10^{-4} **f** 374×10^{-7} **g** 425×10^{38} **h** 0.56×10^{-7}

2 Find the area of this rectangle, leaving your answer in standard form.

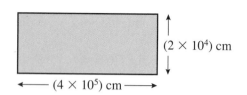

(2×10^4) cm

(4×10^5) cm

3 Work out the following, leaving each answer in standard form.

a $(2 \times 10^8) \times (2 \cdot 5 \times 10^7)$

b $(1 \cdot 5 \times 10^6) \times (4 \times 10^3)$

c $(3 \cdot 5 \times 10^9) \times (2 \times 10^{-4})$

d $(1 \cdot 7 \times 10^{-18}) \times (4 \times 10^{-8})$

e $(4 \times 10^{12}) \times (3 \times 10^7)$

f $(9 \times 10^{17}) \times (4 \times 10^{28})$

g $(8 \times 10^{21}) \div (4 \times 10^6)$

h $(7 \times 10^{19}) \div (2 \times 10^7)$

i $\dfrac{9 \times 10^{32}}{4 \cdot 5 \times 10^{-5}}$

j $(4 \times 10^5)^2$

k $(8 \cdot 7 \times 10^{12}) \div (3 \times 10^{-16})$

l $\dfrac{3 \times 10^{48}}{6 \times 10^{13}}$

4 Five people have collected some money for charity. The amounts are shown in the table below.

Brianna	Matt	Brooke	Vanya	Carter
£$(4 \cdot 116 \times 10^2)$	£$(3 \cdot 02 \times 10^2)$	£$(1 \cdot 01 \times 10^3)$	£$(4 \cdot 3 \times 10)$	£$(1 \cdot 002 \times 10^3)$

List the names in the order of the money they each collected, starting with the greatest amount.

5 Calli has £(4×10^5) and Carl has £(3×10^4). They put their money together. Write down the total amount of money they have, giving your answer in standard form.

6 Work out the following, leaving each answer in standard form.

a $(5 \times 10^6) + (7 \times 10^5)$

b $(9 \times 10^8) - (4 \times 10^7)$

c $(4 \cdot 8 \times 10^{12}) - (1 \cdot 9 \times 10^{11})$

d $(3 \times 10^{-2}) - (9 \times 10^{-3})$

e $(4 \cdot 3 \times 10^{-8}) + (2 \times 10^{-7})$

f $(6 \cdot 4 \times 10^{24}) + (5 \cdot 6 \times 10^{23})$

7 The acceleration a of a particle is given by the formula $a = \dfrac{v - u}{t}$.

Work out the value of a when $u = 5 \cdot 5 \times 10^{-4}$, $t = 2 \times 10^3$ and $v = 6 \cdot 2 \times 10^{-3}$.

8 In a TV popstar show final, the number of votes for each contestant is shown below:

Gary Tallow $\qquad$ $(9 \cdot 6 \times 10^5)$ votes

Nina X $\qquad$ $(1 \cdot 3 \times 10^6)$ votes

Rosa Williams $\qquad$ $(1 \cdot 85 \times 10^6)$ votes

How many people voted in total?

9 Work out $(7 \times 10^{-12})^3$, leaving your answer in standard form.

10 The density of a type of stone is $3 \cdot 5 \times 10^4$ kg/m³. Find the mass of this type of stone if its volume is 20 m³, leaving your answer in standard form.

Use a calculator.

1 The population of the UK is $(5 \cdot 97 \times 10^7)$ people. The population of the USA is $(2 \cdot 41 \times 10^8)$ people. What is the combined population of the UK and USA? (give your answer in standard form)

2 The mass of an atom is $3 \cdot 74 \times 10^{-26}$ grams. What is the total mass of 2 million atoms?

3 Work out the following, leaving each answer in standard form correct to 3 significant figures.

a $\dfrac{(5 \cdot 6 \times 10^{21}) \times (2 \cdot 7 \times 10^{28})}{5 \times 10^{13}}$

b $\dfrac{(7 \cdot 4 \times 10^{-13}) \times (3 \cdot 94 \times 10^{-26})}{4 \cdot 2 \times 10^{18}}$

c $\dfrac{(3 \cdot 8 \times 10^{23}) - (9 \cdot 7 \times 10^{22})}{1 \cdot 8 \times 10^{-17}}$

d $\dfrac{(4 \cdot 89 \times 10^{16})^2}{2 \cdot 14 \times 10^9}$

e $\sqrt{\dfrac{(4 \cdot 83 \times 10^{14}) + (3 \cdot 16 \times 10^{15})}{2 \cdot 82 \times 10^{-12}}}$

f $\dfrac{\sqrt{5 \cdot 28 \times 10^{31}}}{(4 \cdot 9 \times 10^{-10}) + (2 \cdot 7 \times 10^{-9})}$

g $\dfrac{(7 \cdot 3 \times 10^{14})^2}{(3 \cdot 92 \times 10^{-15}) \times (2 \cdot 8 \times 10^{-23})}$

h $\sqrt{\dfrac{(3 \cdot 48 \times 10^{15}) \times (2 \cdot 19 \times 10^{26})}{(4 \cdot 37 \times 10^{12}) + (1 \cdot 95 \times 10^{11})}}$

4 The adult population of a country is 60 million. The average annual income per adult is £27 000. Find in standard form the total annual income from the adult population.

5 In 2010 the population of a country was $9 \cdot 2 \times 10^9$. Over the next five years the population rose by 15%. Find the population in 2015.

6 The diameter of the earth is $1 \cdot 3 \times 10^7 \, \text{m}$. Assuming that the earth is a perfect sphere, find the circumference of the earth. Give your answer in standard form to 2 significant figures.

7 $E = mgh$. Find the value of h to 3 significant figures in standard form if $E = 3 \cdot 78 \times 10^4$, $m = 2 \cdot 3 \times 10^2$ and $g = 9 \cdot 81$.

8 The population of a certain country is $5 \cdot 7 \times 10^8$ and its area is $7 \cdot 21 \times 10^{10} \, \text{m}^2$. Find the population density (people per m^2) of this country. Give your answer in standard form to 2 sig. figs.

9 The population of a certain type of bird increased from $7 \cdot 8 \times 10^3$ to $1 \cdot 2 \times 10^4$ over a ten year period. Find the percentage increase over that period, giving your answer to 3 sig. figs.

10 The speed of light is approximately $2 \cdot 8 \times 10^8 \, \text{m/s}$. Express this in km/h in standard form to 3 sig. figs.

TASK M5.6 ———————————————————————————— **Main Book Page 136**

1 The length of a book is 23·4 cm, measured to the nearest 0·1 cm.

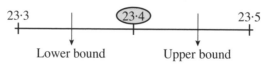

Write down   **a** the lower bound   **b** the upper bound

2 The width of a room is 3·8 m, measured to the nearest 0·1 m.

Write down   **a** the lower bound   **b** the upper bound

3 A woman weighs 63 kg, correct to the nearest kg. What is her least possible weight?

4 Copy and complete the table.

A length l is 47·2 cm, to the nearest 0·1 cm, so		$\leqslant l <$	47·25
A mass m is 83 kg, to the nearest kg, so		$\leqslant m <$	
A Volume V is 7·3 m³, to the nearest 0·1 m³, so		$\leqslant V <$	
A radius r is 6·87 cm, to the nearest 0·01 cm, so		$\leqslant r <$	
An area A is 470 m², to the nearest 10 m², so		$\leqslant A <$	

5 Truncate the actual value of π to 3 decimal places.

6 Write down an inequality for the possible values of x if $x = 36·18$ when truncated to 2 decimal places.

7 The base and height of a triangle are measured to the nearest 0·1 cm.

   a Write down the upper bound for the base 3·4 cm.

   b Write down the lower bound for the height 4·8 cm.

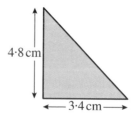

8 The capacity c of a jug is 503·4 ml, measured to the nearest 0·1 ml. Write down the upper and lower bounds as an inequality.

9 In a 200 m race a runner is timed at 23·46 seconds to the nearest 0·01 second. Write down the upper and lower bounds as an inequality.

10 Amelia weighs 64 kg, correct to the nearest 4 kg. John weighs 62 kg, correct to the nearest 1 kg. They sit on opposite sides of a seesaw. If each person's weight is equal to the lower bound, who will sink to the ground? *Explain* your answer fully.

11 Write down an inequality for the upper and lower bounds for each number below:

$d = 360$, correct to the nearest 20
$m = 45$, correct to the nearest 5
$x = 6\cdot4$, correct to the nearest $0\cdot2$

12 Write down an inequality for the possible values of y if $y = 18\cdot174$ when truncated to 3 decimal places.

13 The mass of a substance is measured as $8\cdot5$ g, correct to the nearest $0\cdot5$ g. Write down the least possible mass of the substance.

14 The circumference of a tin is 25 cm, correct to the nearest mm. Identical tins are placed on the shelf shown opposite. What is the least number of tins which should fit on the shelf? *Explain* your answer fully.

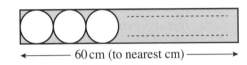
← 60 cm (to nearest cm) →

TASK E5.1 ──────────────────────────── **Main Book Page 139**

1 The length, width and height of the cuboid are measured to the nearest cm.

volume = length × width × height

What is the lowest possible value of the volume of the cuboid?

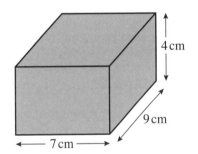
4 cm
9 cm
← 7 cm →

2 If $k = 1\cdot8$, $m = 4\cdot9$ and $n = 8\cdot3$, all measured to one decimal place, calculate:

  a the smallest possible value of kn

  b the largest possible value (to 3 sig. figs.) of $\dfrac{m}{k}$

  c the largest possible value of $m + n - k$

3 The base and height of this triangle are measured to the nearest $0\cdot1$ m. Calculate the lower and upper bounds for the area of this triangle.

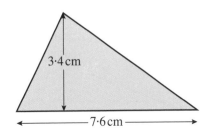
$3\cdot4$ cm
← $7\cdot6$ cm →

4 Each measurement opposite is correct to the nearest millimetre. The volume of the triangular prism is calculated. Work out the greatest possible percentage error with this calculation.

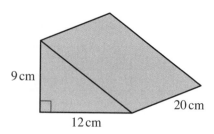

9 cm

20 cm

12 cm

5 The acceleration a after time t can be calculated with the formula

$$a = \frac{v - u}{t}$$

where v is the speed and u is the initial speed. If $v = 23$, $u = 18$ and $t = 39$, measured to the nearest whole number, calculate:

a the minimum possible value for a (to 2 sig. figs.)

b the maximum possible value for a (to 2 sig. figs.)

6 The area of a square is given as 70 cm², correct to the nearest cm².

Find the upper and lower bounds for the length x of one side of the square.

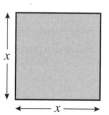

x

x

7 A length is 6·5 cm when rounded to the nearest millimetre and is 6 cm when rounded to the nearest centimetre. Write down an interval for the possible values of the length l.

8 The mass of an object is 50 g to the nearest gram and its volume is 20 cm³ to the nearest cm³. Work out the range of possible values for its density.

9 Pythagoras' theorem states that $a^2 + b^2 = c^2$ where a, b and c are the three lengths of a right-angled triangle and c is the hypotenuse. If $a = 4·3$ cm and $c = 12·1$ cm, both correct to 1 decimal place, find the upper and lower bounds for b.

| **TASK M5.7** | **Main Book Page 143** |

1 m is directly proportional to n.

$m = 48$ when $n = 8$.

Find the value of m when $n = 5$.

2

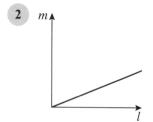

m

l

Chris says that the mass m of a metal bar is directly proportional to its length l. Does the graph opposite support his statement? Explain your answer fully.

3 p is directly proportional to q.

$p = 28$ when $q = 4$.

Find   **a** p when $q = 9$ **b** q when $p = 21$

4 In the following tables, y is directly proportional to x. Copy and complete each table.

a

x	6	11		22
y	54		108	

b

x	6	10		32
y		35	70	

5 Which equations below suggest that y is directly proportional to x?

a $y = \dfrac{3}{x}$ **b** $y = 7x$ **c** $\dfrac{y}{4} = x$ **d** $y = 3x^2$ **e** $y = \dfrac{1}{2}x$

6 $16\,m^2$ of carpet costs £383·84. How much carpet can be bought for £527·78?

7 In an electrical circuit it is known that the voltage V varies as the current I
(ie. that V is directly proportional to I). It is also known that $V = 36$ when $I = 8$.

   a Find V when $I = 14$.

   b Find I when $V = 27$.

8 Write down any equation which you believe is
appropriate for the relationship shown by
the graph opposite.

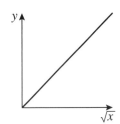

TASK E5.2 ——————————————————————————— **Main Book Page 145**

1 Find k then copy and complete the table below given that $y = kx^3$.

x	3	5		10
y	135		1715	

2 Find k then copy and complete the table below given that $y = k\sqrt{x}$.

x	4	9		100
y	12		48	

3 m is directly proportional to the square root of n.

$m = 6$ when $n = 9$.

a Copy and complete:

$m \propto \sqrt{n}$ so $m = \square\sqrt{n}$

$m = 6, n = 9$ so $6 = \square\sqrt{\square}$

$6 = 3\square$

$\square = 2$

so $m = \square\sqrt{n}$

b Find m when $n = 25$

so $m = \square\sqrt{25} = \square$

4 L is directly proportional to the square of W.

$L = 24$ when $W = 2$.

a Find a formula for L in terms of W.

b Find L when $W = 5$.

c Find W when $L = 96$.

5 P is directly proportional to the cube of Q.

$P = 32$ when $Q = 4$.

a Find a formula for P in terms of Q.

b Find P when $Q = 6$.

c Find Q when $P = 500$.

6 **a** If y is directly proportional to x^2 then by what factor does y increase as x doubles?

    b If y is directly proportional to x^3 then by what factor does y increase as x doubles?

7 The mass M of an object is directly proportional to the cube root of its height H.

$M = 20$ when $H = 64$.

a Find M when $H = 27$.

b Find H when $M = 35$.

TASK M5.8   **Main Book Page 148**

1 y is inversely proportional to x and $y = 16$ when $x = 2$.

    a Find y when $x = 10$.   **b** Find x when $y = 4$.

2 Which equations below suggest that y is inversely proportional to x?

    a $y = \frac{1}{4}x$ **b** $y = \frac{4}{x}$ **c** $xy = 6$ **d** $5y = x$ **e** $4xy = 1$

3 *m* is inversely proportional to p^2. Write down any equation which you believe is appropriate for this relationship.

4 *A* is inversely proportional to *B* and $A = 15$ when $B = 3$.
   a Find *A* when $B = 9$.
   b Find *B* when $A = 60$.

5

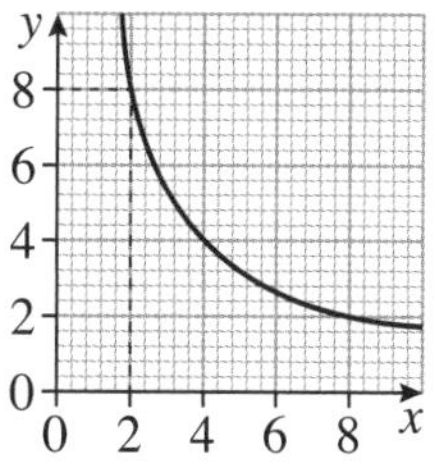

This graph shows that *y* is inversely proportional to *x*.
   a Find *y* when $x = 0.5$
   b Find *x* when $y = \dfrac{1}{4}$

6 *R* is inversely proportional to *I* and $I = 5$ when $R = 3$.
   a Find *R* when $I = 7.5$
   b Find *I* when $R = 30$

7 Find *k* then copy and complete the table below given that $y = \dfrac{k}{x}$

x	1	4	8	
y		5		1

TASK E5.3 ——————————————————————————— **Main Book Page 149**

1 *y* is inversely proportional to the cube root of *x*.
   $y = 30$ when $x = 8$.
   a Write down an equation for *y* in terms of *x*. Copy and complete:

$$y \propto \frac{1}{\sqrt[3]{x}} \qquad \text{so} \qquad y = \frac{k}{\sqrt[3]{x}}$$

$$y = 30,\, x = 8 \qquad \text{so} \qquad 30 = \frac{k}{\sqrt[3]{\Box}}$$

$$30 = \frac{k}{\Box}$$

$$k = \Box$$

$$\text{so} \qquad y = \frac{\Box}{\sqrt[3]{x}}$$

b Find y when $x = 1000$. Copy and complete:

$x = 1000$ so $y = \dfrac{\square}{\sqrt[3]{\square}} = \dfrac{\square}{\square} = \square$

c Find x when $y = 20$. Copy and complete:

$y = 20$ so $20 = \dfrac{\square}{\sqrt[3]{x}}$

$20\sqrt[3]{x} = \square$

$\sqrt[3]{x} = \dfrac{\square}{20} = \square$

$x = \square^3 = \square$

2 m is inversely proportional to the square of v.

$m = 4$ when $v = 5$.

a Find an equation for m in terms of v.

b Find m when $v = 2$.

c Find v when $m = 0 \cdot 25$.

3 The width W of an object is inversely proportional to the cube of its height H.

$W = 2$ when $H = 2$.

a Find an equation for W in terms of H.

b Find W when $H = 4$.

c Find H when $W = \dfrac{1}{32}$.

4 y is inversely proportional to the square root of x.

What happens to y when x is quadrupled?

5 x is inversely proportional to the square root of y.

$x = 3$ when $y = 100$.

a Find x when $y = 16$.

b Find y when $x = 12$.

6 The volume V of a gas is inversely proportional to the pressure P. If $V = V_1$ when $P = P_1$ and $V = V_2$ when $P = P_2$, express V_1 in terms of V_2, P_1 and P_2.

ALGEBRA 2 6

TASK M6.1 — — — — — — — — — **Main Book Page 158**

Solve

1 $\dfrac{n}{4} = 2$ **2** $\dfrac{x}{10} = 6$ **3** $n + 3 = 1$ **4** $y + 2 = 1$

5 $p - 3 = -6$ **6** $3a = -6$ **7** $-5x = -20$ **8** $n \div 3 = -4$

9 $\dfrac{b}{5} = -5$ **10** $\dfrac{m}{7} = -3$ **11** $2y = 1$ **12** $7f = 2$

13 $2n = -3$ **14** $5x = 7$ **15** $7a = -4$ **16** $3m = -11$

17 Find the value of x in this rectangle.

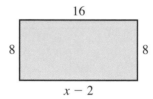

18 Pat thinks of a number and then adds 10.
If the answer is 5, what number did Pat think of?

Solve the following equations

19 $6n + 4 = 16$ **20** $3a - 8 = 19$ **21** $34 = 5y - 6$

22 $4m + 7 = 10$ **23** $9w - 5 = 2$ **24** $8y - 2 = -5$

25 $5x - 3 = 2x + 18$ **26** $9p - 6 = 6p + 18$ **27** $5n + 3 = 27 - n$

28 $3a + 9 = 44 - 2a$ **29** $5w + 19 = 11 - 3w$ **30** $17 - 2x = 29 - 6x$

31 This is an *isosceles* triangle.
Find the value of x.

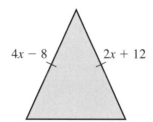

Solve

32 $\dfrac{8}{x} = 12$ **33** $\dfrac{n}{4} + 2 = 8$ **34** $\dfrac{m}{7} - 3 = 4$

35 $\dfrac{4a}{5} = 12$ **36** $\dfrac{6w}{5} = -12$ **37** $\dfrac{48}{c} = -4$

TASK M6.2 ──────────────────────────────── **Main Book Page 159**

Solve

1 $2(2x + 3) = 14$

2 $4(n - 3) = 24$

3 $5(2a - 1) = 25$

4 $5(2w - 6) = 40$

5 $5(2a + 3) = 18$

6 $70 = 10(2 - 5y)$

7 I think of a number. I add 9 onto the number then multiply the answer by 3. This gives 36. What was the number I started with?

Solve the following equations

8 $4(2x + 1) = 2(3x + 5)$

9 $5(3a + 4) = 4(3a + 20)$

10 $2(4y - 3) = 5(y + 6)$

11 $4(3m - 1) = 2(5m + 7)$

12 $5(2n + 4) = 2(4n + 3)$

13 $3(3w + 2) + 5(w + 4) = 54$

14 $8(3q + 4) + 1 = 3(12q - 1)$

15 $5(2x + 1) - 5 = 2(6x + 5)$

16 $7 - 3(2 - 3x) = 10$

17 $3(h - 2) + 2(h - 3) = 28$

18 $4(2p + 7) - 5(p - 1) = 12$

19 $6(2a + 3) - 4 = 4(a + 6) + 6$

20 $3(2w + 7) - 5 = 4(3w - 6) + 35$

21 $2(5x + 3) - 6(2x - 1) = 3(x + 14)$

22 $\frac{1}{5}(3n + 2) + \frac{3}{10}(7n - 12) = 13$

23 $\frac{1}{4}(11w + 5) - \frac{1}{3}(4w + 7) = 6$

TASK M6.3 ──────────────────────────────── **Main Book Page 161**

Solve

1 $\frac{x}{7} - 4 = 4$

2 $\frac{y - 4}{7} = 4$

3 $\frac{a + 9}{4} = 6$

4 $\frac{c}{5} - 3 = 2$

5 $\frac{x - 8}{6} = 5$

6 $\frac{3n + 5}{2} = 3$

7 $\frac{30}{x} = 5$

8 $\frac{7}{a} = 2$

9 $3 = \frac{11}{m}$

Copy and complete:

10 $\frac{20}{x + 3} = 5$

$20 = \boxed{}(x + 3)$

$20 = \boxed{} + \boxed{}$

$20 - \boxed{} = \boxed{}$

$\boxed{} = \boxed{}$

$x = \boxed{}$

11 $\frac{6 - 7n}{2n + 4} = -3$

$6 - 7n = -3(\boxed{} + \boxed{})$

$6 - 7n = \boxed{} - \boxed{}$

$6 + \boxed{} = \boxed{} + 7n$

$\boxed{} = \boxed{}$

$n = \boxed{}$

Solve the following equations

12 $\dfrac{15}{a + 1} = 3$

13 $\dfrac{21}{n - 2} = 7$

14 $\dfrac{10}{2y + 1} = 5$

15 $\dfrac{1 - 2m}{3} = 5$

16 $\dfrac{8}{w} + 3 = 7$

17 $\dfrac{5x + 7}{2x - 2} = 3$

18 $\dfrac{7f - 2}{3f - 1} = 5$

19 $\dfrac{3n + 2}{2n - 3} = 7$

20 $\dfrac{11z - 1}{5z - 2} = 3$

21 $\dfrac{6a - 1}{5a - 4} = 2$

22 $4 = \dfrac{6x + 5}{2x - 1}$

23 $\dfrac{7v + 3}{6v + 1} = 2$

| **TASK M6.4** | **Main Book Page 162** |

1 **a** Write down an equation using the angles.

b Find x.

c Write down the actual value of each angle in this quadrilateral.

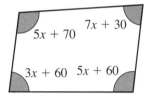

2 The length of a rectangle is 8 cm more than its width. If its perimeter is 44 cm, find its width.

3 Hannah has 3 times as much money as Joe. Hannah spends £24 on a new blouse. She now has £30 left. How much money has Joe got?

4 This is an *isosceles* triangle.

a Find the value of x.

b Find the perimeter of the triangle.

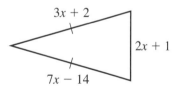

5 The area of this rectangle is 60 cm².

a Write down an equation involving x.

b Find x.

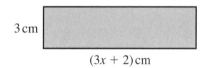

6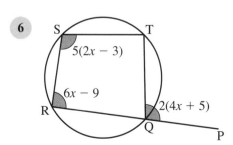

$\widehat{QRS} = 6x - 9$

$\widehat{RST} = 5(2x - 3)$

$\widehat{PQT} = 2(4x + 5)$

Calculate the value of $\widehat{STQ}$.

7 Three consecutive whole numbers add up to 144. If the lowest number is n,

    a write down an expression for the other two numbers in terms of n.

    b write down an equation involving n.

    c find n then write down the three consecutive whole numbers.

8 The area of each rectangle is equal (all lengths are measured in cm).

    a Find the value of x.

    b Find the area of one of the rectangles.

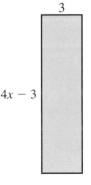
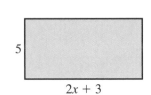

9 The velocity, v of a particle is given by the formula

    $$v = u + 17t$$

    where u is its initial velocity and t is the time taken.

    Its velocity reaches four times its initial velocity when $t = 6$ seconds.

    Find its initial velocity in m/s.

10 Find the actual length and width of this rectangle.

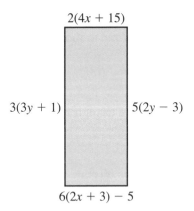

TASK M6.5   **Main Book Page 165**

1 $a = b - 10$ Make b the subject of the formula.

2 $n = 5m$ Make m the subject of the formula.

3 Write down the pairs of equations which belong to each other.

    A $\left(\, y = 8x \,\right)$ **B** $\left(\, y = \frac{x}{8} \,\right)$ **C** $\left(\, 8y = x \,\right)$ **D** $\left(\, \frac{y}{8} = x \,\right)$

4 Write down which working out below is correct.

a $m = 4n + 8$
  $m + 8 = 4n$
  $\dfrac{m + 8}{4} = n$

b $y = 2x - 6$
  $y + 6 = 2x$
  $\dfrac{y + 6}{2} = x$

5 Make n the subject of each formula given below:

a $m = cn - f$

b $x = gn + h$

c $an - 2m = y$

d $m(n + p) = v$

e $x(n + f) = y$

f $h(n - 3) = x$

g $y = \dfrac{n}{8} - 2$

h $q = w(n - p)$

i $\dfrac{n}{y} + f = 3g$

6 $\dfrac{an - b}{3} = c$ Make n the subject of the formula.

7 $\dfrac{mx + c}{a} = b$ Make x the subject of the formula.

8 $y = \dfrac{3(b + c)}{m}$ Make b the subject of the formula.

9 Make x the subject of each formula given below:

a $a(x + b) = c$

b $\dfrac{x + p}{q} = r$

c $\dfrac{p(x + q)}{r} = t$

d $\dfrac{h}{x} = u$

e $\dfrac{k}{x + b} = w$

f $\dfrac{d}{ax + b} = c$

10 Make w the subject of each formula given below:

a $a - bw = c$

b $\dfrac{p - qw}{r} = y$

c $h - \dfrac{w}{g} = k$

d $\dfrac{w + t}{m} = p - q$

e $b^2 - a(w + b) = c$

f $y = \dfrac{aw + b}{q} - c$

TASK M6.6 ──────────────────────────── **Main Book Page 167**

1 Copy and complete:

a $\sqrt{x} + b = a$

$\sqrt{x} = a - \square$

$x = (a - \square)^2$

b $\sqrt{(x + b)} = a$

$x + b = \square$

$x = \square - \square$

c $x^3 + w = 6m$

$x^3 = 6m - \square$

$x = \sqrt[\square]{(6m - \square)}$

2 Make x the subject of each formula given below:

a $x^2 + b = c$ **b** $px^2 + q = r$ **c** $ax^2 = b$

d $\dfrac{ax^2}{b} = c$ **e** $\sqrt{x} - m = w$ **f** $\dfrac{\sqrt{x} + u}{v} = z$

g $\dfrac{a\sqrt{x} + b}{c} = d$ **h** $a - x^3 = b$ **i** $\dfrac{\sqrt{(x - p)}}{t} = r$

3 $v^2 = u^2 + 2as$ Make u the subject of the formula.

4 $A = 4\pi r^3$ Make r the subject of the formula.

5 $w = up + 4aq^2$ Make a the subject of the formula.

6 $A = 8(w - p)^2$ Make w the subject of the formula.

7 Make n the subject of each formula given below:

a $h = \dfrac{m}{n}$ **b** $\dfrac{n}{v} - x = w$ **c** $h - \dfrac{n}{g} = k$

d $\dfrac{a}{n} + q = p$ **e** $\dfrac{b}{n + c} = m$ **f** $y = \dfrac{6a}{n - w}$

8 $\dfrac{h + a}{b} = \dfrac{x + d}{c}$ Make x the subject of the formula.

9 $T = \sqrt{\left(\dfrac{w - a}{g}\right)}$ Make w the subject of the formula.

10 Make y the subject of each formula given below:

a $\sqrt{\left(\dfrac{y}{m}\right)} = h$ **b** $\sqrt[3]{(y - z)} = r$ **c** $A = \dfrac{1}{2}my^3$

d $\sqrt[3]{(ay - b)} = c$ **e** $\sqrt{(my + n)} = p$ **f** $v - y^3 = a$

g $py^3 - q = x$ **h** $\sqrt{\left(\dfrac{y - m}{n}\right)} = w$ **i** $x = \dfrac{\sqrt[3]{(my + p)}}{3}$

TASK M6.7   **Main Book Page 169**

1 Copy and complete:

a $ax - b = cx$

$ax - cx = \square$

$x(\square - \square) = \square$

$x = \dfrac{\square}{\square - \square}$

b $\dfrac{v + 3w}{v} = p$

$v + 3w = \square$

$3w = \square - \square$

$3w = v(\square - \square)$

$v = \dfrac{3w}{\square - \square}$

2 Make x the subject of each formula given below:

a $cx + f = mx$ **b** $mx - w = px$ **c** $ax + b = cx + d$

d $a(x - c) = b(x + f)$ **e** $4x = m(x + y)$ **f** $p + qx = m(n - x)$

3 Make x the subject of the formula $a = \dfrac{c + bx}{x}$

4 Make m the subject of the formula $m = \dfrac{d + em}{a}$

5 Make w the subject of the formula $\dfrac{aw}{w + b} = c$

6 Make v the subject of the formula $\dfrac{p - qv}{r - sv} = t$

7 Make q the subject of the formula $\dfrac{kq}{q + b} = e$

8 Make n the subject of each formula given below:

a $\sqrt{\dfrac{a - bn}{n}} = c$ **b** $\sqrt{\dfrac{n - 1}{n}} = t$ **c** $b = \sqrt[3]{\dfrac{n}{n + a}}$

d $\left(\dfrac{n - c}{n}\right)^2 = a$ **e** $y = \left(\dfrac{m + n}{n}\right)^3$ **f** $\sqrt{\dfrac{n - w}{n - x}} = p$

9 $\dfrac{aw + y}{c} = \dfrac{bw + u}{d}$ Make w the subject of the formula.

10 $P = \dfrac{1}{x}\left(\dfrac{WQ}{R} - M\right)$ Make R the subject of the formula.

TASK E6.1   **Main Book Page 171**

1 If $f(x) = 3x + 6$, find the value of:

a $f(2)$ **b** $f(-4)$ **c** $f(-1)$ **d** $f(200)$

2 If $g(x) = x^3$, find the value of:

a $g(3)$ **b** $g(-1)$ **c** $g(-4)$ **d** $g\left(\dfrac{1}{2}\right)$

3 If $h(x) = (x + 3)^2$, find the value of:

a $h(4)$ **b** $h(0)$ **c** $h(-2)$ **d** $h(p)$

4 If $f(x) = \dfrac{x^2 + 3x - 1}{x + 4}$, find the value of:

a $f(0)$ **b** $f(1)$ **c** $f(-1)$ **d** $f(w)$

5 If $f(x) = 2x + 7$, find the value of x when $f(x) = 23$.

6 If $g(x) = 4x - 18$, find the value of x when $g(x) = -26$.

7 If $h(x) = \dfrac{5 - 3x}{7}$, find the value of x when $h(x) = -4$.

8 If $g(x) = x^2 - 3x$, find the values of x when $g(x) = 18$.

9 If $f(x) = x^2 + 8$, find the values of w when $f(w) = 6w$.

10 If $f(x) = 14$, find the value(s) of x when

    a $f(x) = 20 - 2x$ **b** $f(x) = x^2 - 5x$ **c** $f(x) = x^2 - 8x + 14$

11 If $g(x) = 3x + 2$, write down each function below:

    a $g(x) - 6$ **b** $4g(x) + 1$ **c** $5 - g(x)$ **d** $2 - 6g(x)$

12 If $f(x) = 5x - 3$ and $g(x) = 2x + 9$, solve $f(x) + 4 = 3 - g(x)$

13 If $f(x) = 4x + 5$ then $f(x - 3) = 4(x - 3) + 5 = 4x - 7$

    Write down the function $f(2x + 1)$.

14 If $g(x) = 3x - 6$, write down each function below:

    a $g(x + 4)$ **b** $g(2x)$ **c** $g(-x)$

15 If $f(x) = x^2 - 4x - 6$ and $g(x) = 5 - \dfrac{1}{2}x^2$, find the values of x for which $\dfrac{1}{2}f(x) = g(x)$.

16 If $f(x) = 3x - 1$, show that $f(4x) + 2f(3x) = m(10x - 1)$ where m is an integer to be found.

TASK E6.2   **Main Book Page 174**

1 Find $f^{-1}(x)$ for each function below:

    a $f(x) = 6x + 5$ **b** $f(x) = \dfrac{3x + 5}{7}$ **c** $f(x) = 2(3x + 2) - 8$

2 $f(x) = \dfrac{4x - 1}{3} + 6$

    a Find $f^{-1}(x)$ **b** Find $f^{-1}(9)$

3 If $f(x) = 4x - 7$, find the value of $f(13) + f^{-1}(13)$.

4 $f(x) = \dfrac{x}{4} + 3$ and $g(x) = 4x^3 - 1$

    Solve $f^{-1}(x) = g^{-1}(107)$

5 Solve $f^{-1}(x) = 2$ if $f(x) = 5(2x + 3)$

6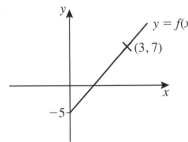

Based on the graph opposite, work out $f^{-1}(-13)$.

7 $f(x) = \dfrac{x}{3} + 1$

Find the set of values of x for which $f^{-1}(x) < 15$

8 $f(x) = 5x + 3$

Solve $f(x) - f^{-1}(x) = 18$

9 $f(x) = \dfrac{4}{x} - 2$ and $g(x) = 3x^3 - 23$

Solve $f^{-1}(x) = g(2)$

10 $f(x) = 4x - 6$ and $g(x) = 2x + 7$

Solve $f^{-1}(x) = g^{-1}(x)$

TASK E6.3	**Main Book Page 176**

1 $f(x) = x^3 - 1$ $\qquad$ $g(x) = 5(2x + 3)$ $\qquad$ $h(x) = 7x - 4$

Find the following composite functions:

a $gf(x)$ $\qquad\qquad$ **b** $fh(x)$ $\qquad\qquad$ **c** $hg(x)$

d $hh(x)$ $\qquad\qquad$ **e** $gh(x)$ $\qquad\qquad$ **f** $gg(x)$

2 $f(x) = 4x + 1$ $\qquad$ $g(x) = \dfrac{1}{2}(x - 6)$

Find **a** $fg(12)$ $\qquad$ **b** $ff(-2)$ $\qquad$ **c** $gf(2)$

3 If $f(x) = \dfrac{x}{4}$ and $g(x) = 5x - 1$, solve $gf(x) = f(x)$

4 If $f(x) = x^2 + 1$ and $g(x) = x + 2$, solve $fg(x) = f(x)$

5 $f(x) = \dfrac{x}{3} - 2$ and $g(x) = 6x + 9$

Find the set of values for which $fg(x) \geqslant g(x)$

6 $f(x) = 3x + 2$ and $g(x) = 4x + 1$

a Solve $gf(x) = f(x)$ $\qquad\qquad$ **b** Solve $gf(x) = f(3x)$

7 If $f(x) = 5x$ and $g(x) = 2x + 9$, find

   a $g^{-1}(x)$ **b** $fg^{-1}(x)$ **c** $f^{-1}(x)$

   d $gf^{-1}(45)$ **e** $g^{-1}f^{-1}(15)$ **f** $gf^{-1}g^{-1}(x)$

8 If $f(x) = x + 4$ and $g(x) = x^2 - 5x$, solve $gf(x) = 0$

9 If $f(x) = 4(2x - 3)$ and $g(x) = \dfrac{6}{x}$, solve $f^{-1}(x) = fg^{-1}(3)$

10 $f(x) = 4x + 1$ $g(x) = 2x - 3$ $h(x) = 2(x + 3)$

   Solve $hgh^{-1}(15x) = fg^{-1}(5x)$

| **TASK E6.4** | **Main Book Page 179** |

1 The area of this rectangle is 42 cm^2.
This means that $x(x + 4) = 42$
Copy and complete the table below to find x to
one decimal place by trial and improvement.

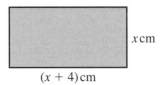

x cm

$(x + 4)$ cm

Trial	Calculation	Too large or too small?
$x = 5$	$5 \times 9 = 45$	too large
$x = 4$	$4 \times 8 = 32$	too small
$x = 4{\cdot}5$	$4{\cdot}5 \times 8{\cdot}5 = 38{\cdot}25$	too ...
$x = 4{\cdot}7$	$4{\cdot}7 \times 8{\cdot}7 = \ldots$	too ...
$x = 4{\cdot}9$	$4{\cdot}9 \times 8{\cdot}9 = \ldots$	too ...
$x = 4{\cdot}8$	$4{\cdot}8 \times 8{\cdot}8 = \ldots$	too ...
$x = 4{\cdot}75$	$4{\cdot}75 \times 8{\cdot}75 = \ldots$	too ...
Answer: $x = \ldots$ (to one decimal place)		

2 Solve these equations by trial and improvement. Give each answer to 1 decimal place.

   a $x(x - 3) = 36$ **b** $x^2 + x = 77$

3 A cube of side length x has a hole
cut through it as shown.
A prism with end area equal to 3
and length x is removed.
The volume of the solid remaining is 140.
Form an equation and use trial and
improvement to find the value of x to
1 decimal place.

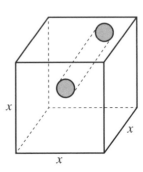

4 Solve these equations by trial and improvement. Give each answer to 2 decimal places.

   a $x^3 - x = 467$ **b** $x(x^2 + 5x) = 84$ **c** $4^x = 76$

1 Use the *interval bisection method* to solve the equation below to 2 decimal places. Use an initial interval of $x = 6$ to 7.

$$x^2 + 5x = 70$$

2 The equation $x^3 - 8x - 7 = 0$ is rearranged into the form $x = \sqrt[3]{(8x + 7)}$ so an iterative formula is $x_{n+1} = \sqrt[3]{(8x_n + 7)}$

Use *fixed point iteration* with $x_1 = 3$ to find a value of x to 2 decimal places.

3 **a** Use *fixed point iteration* with the formula $x_{n+1} = \sqrt{\dfrac{5}{x_n + 3}}$

Use the initial value $x_1 = 2$ and find the value of x to 2 decimal places.

b Rearrange the iterative formula into the form $ax^3 + bx^2 + c = 0$ where a, b and c are integers.

c Write down the cubic equation which has one of its roots (solutions) equal to the x-value found in part **a**.

4

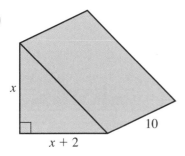

The volume of this prism is 196 cm^3.
All lengths shown are in cm.

a Explain why $5x^2 + 10x = 196$

b Use the *interval bisection method* to find x to 2 decimal places.

5 The diagram opposite shows a semi-circle joined to a right-angled triangle. All lengths shown are in cm. The total area of the semi-circle and the triangle is 48 cm^2.

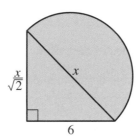

a Use the areas to form an equation in terms of x.

b Take out the common factor x and re-arrange to express x in terms of x. Use *fixed point iteration* with an initial value $x_1 = 8$ to find the value of x to 2 decimal places.

TASK M6.8 ———————————————————————— **Main Book Page 183**

1 **a** Write down the equation of the line which passes through P and R.

   b Write down the equation of the line which passes through S and U.

   c Write down the equation of the line which passes through P and Q.

   d Write down the equation of the line which passes through W, Q and V.

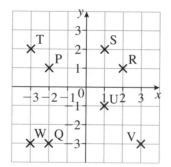

2 Using x-values from 0 to 4, complete a table then draw the straight line $y = 4x + 1$ (make sure you draw the axes big enough).

3 Copy and complete the table below then draw the straight line $y = 4 - x$.

x	0	1	2	3
y				

4 Using x-values from -3 to 3, complete a table then draw the straight line $y = 2x + 3$.

5 Draw the graph of $y = 5 - 4x$

TASK M6.9 ———————————————————————— **Main Book Page 185**

1 **a** Copy and complete the table below then draw the curve $y = x^2 + 2$

x	-3	-2	-1	0	1	2	3
y							

   b Write down the co-ordinates of the turning point (vertex).

2 **a** Copy and complete the table below then draw the curve $y = x^2 + 4x$.

x	-5	-4	-3	-2	-1	0	1	2
x^2				4				4
$+4x$				-8				8
y				-4				12

   b Write down the co-ordinates of
      i the turning point, **ii** the y-intercept and **iii** the intercepts with the x-axis.

3 Repeat question **2** for the curve $y = x^2 + 5x - 4$

4 **a** Draw the graph of $y = 2x^2 - x + 5$ for x-values from -3 to 3.

b Write down the co-ordinates of
i the turning point, **ii** the y-intercept and **iii** the intercepts with the x-axis.

| TASK M6.10 | Main Book Page 188 |

1 **a** Copy and complete the table below then draw the curve $y = x^3 - 2x + 1$.

x	-3	-2	-1	0	1	2	3
x^3		-8					
$-2x$		$+4$					
$+1$	$+1$	$+1$					
y		-3					

b Write down the co-ordinates of the y-intercept.

c Write down the co-ordinates of the turning points.

2 **a** Draw the graph of $y = x^3 - 2x^2 + 3$ for x-values from -2 to 4.
b Write down the co-ordinates of the y-intercept.
c Write down the co-ordinates of the turning points.

3 **a** Draw the graph of $y = \dfrac{20}{x - 1}$ for x-values from -4 to 6. (Be careful when $x = 1$.)

b Use the graph to estimate the x-value when $y = -8$.

4 1. 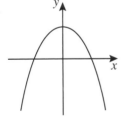   2. 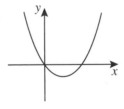   3.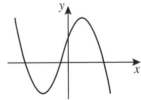

4. 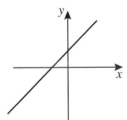   5. 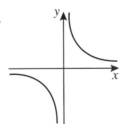   6.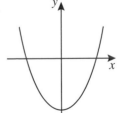

Match each equation to its graph above. One of the equations does not have a graph above.

A $y = \dfrac{5}{x}$ **B** $y = x^2 - 10$ **C** $y = x^2 - x$ **D** $y = 1 - 4x$

E $y = 6 - x^2$ **F** $y = 5 + 7x - x^3$ **G** $y = 4x + 1$

68

1. Copy these axes and sketch the graph of a car travelling at a steady speed then accelerating rapidly.

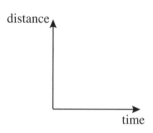

2.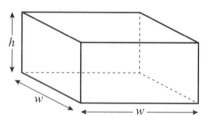

   The graph shows a car journey from Manchester.
   a How far from Manchester is the car at 10:30?
   b When is the car half way between B and C?
   c At what time is the car 30 km from Manchester?
   d Find the speed (in km/h) of the car from B to C.
   e Find the speed (in km/h) of the car from C to D.

3. The pressure P of a quantity of gas is given by the formula $P = \dfrac{50}{V}$ where V is the volume.
   a Draw a graph of P against V for values of V from 1 to 8.
   b Use the graph to find the value of P when $V = 3.5$.
   c Use the graph to find the value of V when $P = 11$.

4. The volume of this *open box* is 10 cm³.
   a Prove that $h = \dfrac{10}{w^2}$

   b Prove that the surface area A is given by
   $A = \dfrac{40}{w} + w^2$

   c Draw a graph of A against w for values of w from 1 to 5.
   d What is the minimum possible surface area?
   e What value of w will give this minimum surface area?

1 Find the gradient of each line below:

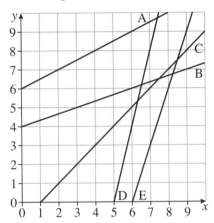

> **Remember:**
>
> Gradient = $\dfrac{\text{vertical distance}}{\text{horizontal distance}}$

2 For each line below, find the rate of change of y as x varies.

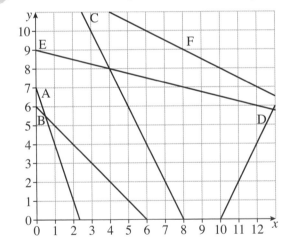

3 Find the gradient of the line joining each pair of points below:

  a $(2, 4)$ and $(3, 7)$ **b** $(1, 0)$ and $(4, 5)$ **c** $(1, 4)$ and $(3, 2)$

  d $(1, 5)$ and $(5, 2)$ **e** $(-3, -2)$ and $(1, -10)$ **f** $(4, -1)$ and $(6, -4)$

4 A line passes through the points $(2, 6)$ and $(5, y)$.
   If the gradient of the line is -3, write down the value of y.

5 For each line below, find the rate of change of y as x varies
(look at the numbers on the axes very carefully):

a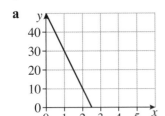

b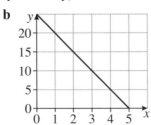

TASK M6.13   **Main Book Page 195**

1 The equation of each line is shown below:

(A) $y = -2x + 6$ (B) $y = -2x + 2$

(C) $y = -2x$ (D) $y = -2x - 3$

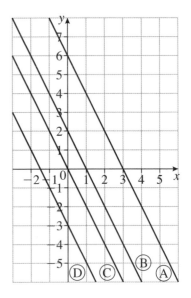

a Use the graph to find the gradient of
lines (A), (B), (C) and (D).

b What do you notice about the gradient
of each line and its equation?

c Look at where each line cuts the y-axis.
For each line, what do you notice about
this value and its equation?

2 **a** Draw the following lines using the same set of axes:

$y = 3x + 4$ $y = 3x + 1$ $y = 3x$ $y = 3x - 2$ $y = 3x - 3$

b Find the gradient of each line. What do you notice about the gradient of each
line and its equation?

c Look at where each line cuts the y-axis. For each line, what do you notice
about this value and its equation?

TASK M6.14   **Main Book Page 197**

1 Which lines below are parallel?

$y = 5x + 1$ $y = 3x + 1$ $y = 1 - 5x$ $y = 5x + 4$ $y = 3 + 5x$

2 Which lines below cut the y-axis at the same point?

$y = 3x + 2$ $y = 2 + 4x$ $y = 3x - 2$ $y = 2x + 3$ $y = 2x$

3 Write down **i** the gradient and **ii** the y-intercept of each line below:

a $y = 8x + 4$ **b** $y = 2x - 6$ **c** $y = x$ **d** $y = x - 5$

e $y = 4 - 2x$ **f** $y = \frac{1}{4}x + 3$ **g** $y + 3x = 2$ **h** $7x - y = 6$

i $2y - 4x = 6$ **j** $3y + 2x = 1$ **k** $5x + 2y = 7$ **l** $4x - 5y - 3 = 0$

4 Write down the equation of each of the 3 lines shown.

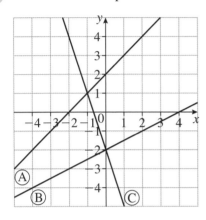

5 Find the equation of the straight line which passes through $(0, 5)$ and has a gradient of 6.

6 Find the equation of the straight line which passes through $(1, 5)$ and has a gradient of 2.

7 Write down the equation of each line shown below:

a

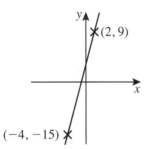

b

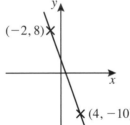

8 Find the equation of the straight line which passes through $(-6, 12)$ and $(2, 8)$.

9 Find the equation of the line that is parallel to the line $3x - y = 2$ and passes through $(6, 5)$.

10 Line l_1 passes through $(4, 1)$ and $(6, -3)$.
Line l_2 is parallel to line l_1 and passes through $(1, -5)$.
Find the equation of line l_2.

TASK E6.7 ──────────────────────────── **Main Book Page 198**

1 Draw an x-axis from -8 to 8 and a y-axis from -8 to 8.

   a Draw $y = x - 1$

   b Draw the line perpendicular to $y = x - 1$ which has the same y-intercept.

   c Find the equation of the line drawn in part **b**.

   d *Multiply* together the gradients of the 2 lines you have drawn.

2 Draw an x-axis from -8 to 8 and a y-axis from -8 to 8.

   a Draw $y = 2x + 1$

   b Draw the line perpendicular to $y = 2x + 1$ which passes through $(2, 5)$

   c Find the equation of the line drawn in part **b**.

   d *Multiply* together the gradients of the 2 lines you have drawn.

3   **a** If the gradient of the line $y = 5x + 3$ is multiplied by the gradient of a line perpendicular to $y = 5x + 3$, what number would be obtained?

   b Write down the gradient of a line which is perpendicular to $y = 5x + 3$.

TASK E6.8 ──────────────────────────── **Main Book Page 200**

1 Write down the gradient of the line which is perpendicular to a line with each gradient given below:

   a 4   **b** 9   **c** -2 **d** 6   **e** -1 **f** $\frac{1}{5}$

   g $\frac{3}{7}$ **h** $-\frac{1}{3}$ **i** $-\frac{2}{5}$ **j** -0.25 **k** 0.1 **l** $\frac{13}{5}$

2 Write down the gradient of any line which is perpendicular to each line shown below:

   a   **b**

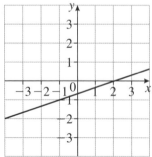 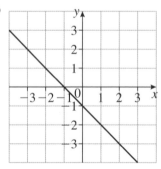

   c Write down the equation of the line which is perpendicular to the line shown in part **a** and passes through $(0, 2)$.

   d Write down the equation of the line which is perpendicular to the line shown in part **b** and has the same y-intercept.

3 A line passes through $(0, -3)$ and is perpendicular to the line $y = 4x + 3$.
Find the equation of the line.

4 A line passes through $(2, 13)$ and is perpendicular to the line $y = -\dfrac{1}{2}x + 5$.
Find the equation of the line.

5 A line passes through $(3, 11)$ and is *parallel* to the line $y = 3x - 4$.
Find the equation of the line.

6 Which of the lines below are perpendicular to the line $3x + y = 4$?

$\boxed{x - 3y = 6}$ $\boxed{y = 3x - 2}$ $\boxed{x + 3y = 1}$ $\boxed{y = 1 - 3x}$ $\boxed{y = \dfrac{1}{3}x + 5}$

7 Find the equation of the line which passes through the given point and is perpendicular to the given line.

a $(1, 11)$ $x + 6y = 6$ **b** $(3, 8)$ $x + 3y = 12$
c $(6, 7)$ **d** $(-3, -3)$

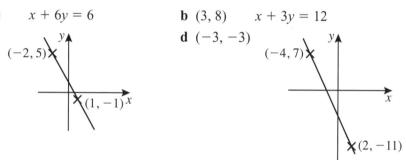

8 Explain clearly why the line $2x + 3y = 1$ is perpendicular to the line $3x - 2y = -4$.

9 A line joins A$(4, 1)$ to B$(8, -3)$.
The midpoint of AB is $(6, -1)$.
Find the equation of the perpendicular bisector of the line AB.

10 Line l_1 passes through $(-2, 5)$ and $(-6, 7)$.
Line l_2 is perpendicular to l_1 and passes through $(-3, 1)$.
Find the equation of line l_2.

TASK E6.9 ———————————————————— **Main Book Page 203**

1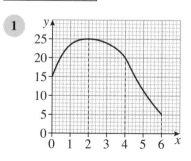

Use the trapezium rule with
3 strips to estimate the area
under the curve shown
opposite.

2 Draw the curve $y = x^3$ for x-values from 0 to 2.
Use the trapezium rule with 4 strips to estimate the area under the curve between $x = 0$ and $x = 2$.

3 Use the trapezium rule with 4 strips to estimate the area under the curve shown opposite between $x = 0$ and $x = 80$.

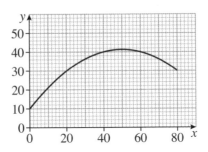

4 The table below shows some $f(x)$ values for $y = f(x)$ between $x = 0$ and $x = 35$.

x	0	5	10	15	20	25	30	35
$f(x)$	4	7	9	12	11	8	9	6

Estimate the area under the curve $y = f(x)$ between $x = 0$ and $x = 35$ using the trapezium rule with 7 strips.

5 Use the trapezium rule with 6 strips to estimate the area under the curve $y = \dfrac{5}{x^2}$ between $x = 1$ and $x = 4$. Give the final answer to 2 decimal places.

TASK E6.10 ──────────────────────────── **Main Book Page 205**

1

Remember:
Average rate of change between A and B is
$$\frac{\text{difference in vertical values}}{\text{difference in horizontal values}}$$

a Work out the gradient of the tangent at C.

b Work out the gradient of the curve at C.

c Work out the average rate of change between A and B.

2 Draw $y = x^2 + 4x - 1$ for x-values from -3 to 2 then find the gradient at $x = 1$.

3 **a** Draw $y = 2^x$ for x-values from 0 to 3.
  b Find the gradient of this curve at $x = 2$.
  c Find the difference between the gradient at $x = 3$ to the gradient at $x = 2$.

4 The graph opposite shows the growth rate of a puppy during a 7 week period.

Work out the rate of growth of the puppy after 2 weeks.

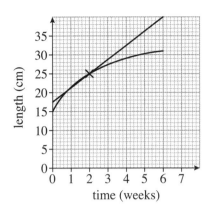

5 A substance decays over a two month period.
Its mass (in grams) is recorded in the table below.

Time (months)	0	0·5	1	1·5	2
Mass (g)	2	0·67	0·22	0·07	0·02

a Draw a graph of mass against time (use at least 2 cm for each unit on both axes).

b Work out the rate of decay of the substance after 0·5 months.

c Find the average rate of decrease of the mass between a time of 0·5 months and 2 months.

TASK E6.11 ──────────────────────────────────── **Main Book Page 207**

1

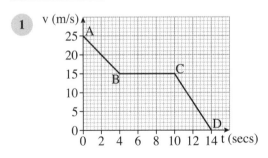

This velocity–time graph shows the motion of a particle.
Find

a the acceleration from A to B (in m/s²).
Note that this will be a negative value because the particle is decelerating.

b the total distance travelled from A to D.

2 A car starts from rest and accelerates uniformly to a speed of 15 m/s in 10 seconds.
It then travels at a constant speed of 15 m/s for 15 seconds.
The car then accelerates uniformly at 1 m/s² until it reaches a speed of 30 m/s.

a Draw a velocity–time graph for the above information.

b How long does the car take to travel the first 150 m?

c Find the acceleration during the first 10 seconds of the motion.

d Find the total distance covered by the car until it reaches the speed of 30 m/s.

3 The graph opposite shows a plane accelerating and decelerating.

   a Work out the acceleration after 5 seconds.

   b Work out the deceleration after 25 seconds.

   c Estimate the distance travelled in the first 25 seconds (hint: use the trapezium rule with 5 strips).

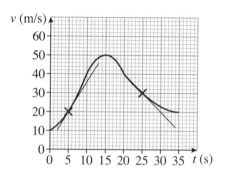

4 A particle moves such that its velocity v(m/s) is given by $v = 1 + 6t - t^2$ where t is the time in seconds.

   a Draw the graph of v against t.

   b Find the acceleration when $t = 1$ second.

   c Estimate the distance travelled in the first 6 seconds.

   d Write down the acceleration when its velocity is 10 m/s.

5

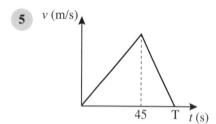

The total distance travelled by a particle is 550 m. The maximum velocity reached is 72 km/h. Its velocity–time graph is shown opposite.

   a Calculate the value of T.

   b How far does the particle travel during the first 18 seconds?

TASK E6.12 ──────────────────────────── **Main Book Page 211**

Assume constant acceleration for all questions in this Exercise.

> **Remember:**
>
> $v = u + at$ $\qquad s = ut + \frac{1}{2}at^2$ $\qquad v^2 = u^2 + 2as$ $\qquad s = \frac{1}{2}(u + v)t$

1 A car has a constant acceleration of 2 m/s².
How long will it take to cover 128 m if it starts at a speed of 8 m/s?

2 A cat is running at a speed of 7 m/s.
Over a 4 second period it accelerates uniformly at a rate of 0·3 m/s².
How far does the cat travel during these 4 seconds?

3 A roller coaster car decelerates uniformly at 2·5 m/s² from a speed of 16 m/s until it stops.
Find the distance it travels before it stops.

4 A ball is projected upwards with a speed of 14 m/s. Its acceleration is $-9\cdot8\,\text{m/s}^2$.

    a Find its speed when it has travelled 5 m upwards.

    b What is the maximum height the ball reaches?

    c How long does the ball take to reach its starting point?

5 A strong wind blows a tile off a roof. If the tile falls 5 m, at what speed will it hit the ground ($a = 9\cdot8\,\text{m/s}^2$)?

6 A grand prix driver accelerates from 180 km/h to 216 km/h with uniform acceleration of $4\,\text{m/s}^2$. He then continues at 216 km/h for 6 seconds before reducing his speed back to 180 km/h with uniform deceleration $3\,\text{m/s}^2$.

    a Find the total time taken to complete all the above.

    b Find the total distance travelled whilst completing all the above.

7 A player in a curling game releases a stone with an initial speed of 12 m/s. It travels 45 m in 6 seconds. Find the deceleration of the stone.

8

P   Q   R

$t = 0$ $\gg a$ $t = 6$ $\gg a$ $t = 10$
$s = 0$ $s = 24$ $s = 54$

A particle is moving in a straight line with constant acceleration, a.
It passes points P, Q and R at times $t = 0$, $t = 6\,\text{s}$, $t = 10\,\text{s}$ respectively.
The distance PQ = 24 m and QR = 30 m.
Consider separately the motion from P to Q and the motion from Q to R in order to find

    a the acceleration   **b** the speed of the particle at P.

STATISTICS 1   8

TASK M8.1   **Main Book Page 232**

1 Freddie throws a coin 120 times. The coin lands on 'tails' 58 times.

    a From Freddie's results, find the *relative frequency* of getting 'tails'.

$$\left(\text{relative frequency} = \frac{\text{number of times event happens}}{\text{total number of trials}}\right)$$

    b Do you think the coin is fair? *Explain* the answer you give.

2 Jo is throwing an 8-sided dice. She throws the dice 240 times. The table below shows her results.

Score	1	2	3	4	5	6	7	8
Frequency	27	24	36	27	30	27	33	36

    a How many times should each number come up if the dice is fair?

    b From Jo's results, *use a calculator* to find the relative frequency of getting each score (1 up to 8).

    c Do you think the dice is fair? *Explain* the answer you give.

3 Mary keeps throwing a drawing pin to find out how many times it will land 'point down'. The table below shows the total number of times the drawing pin has landed 'point down' after every 20 throws.

Number of throws	20	40	60	80	100	120	140	160	180	200
Number of 'point down'	5	13	21	26	36	47	53	59	68	76

    a Work out the relative frequency of the drawing pin landing 'point down' after every 20 throws (round off to 2 decimal places if necessary).

    b Plot a graph of the relative frequency of 'point down' against the total number of throws.

    c Write down the number around which the relative frequency of 'point down' is settling.

4 Five people throw a biased dice several times. They record how many times the dice lands on a '2'.

Name	Number of throws	Number of 2's	Relative frequency
Helena	100	41	0·41
Sandeep	200	83	0·415
Rory	150	60	0·4
Natalie	450	99	0·22
Ben	700	273	0·39

One of these five people made a mistake when recording the number of 2's. Who do you think this was? Give a reason for your answer.

TASK M8.2   **Main Book Page 234**

1 Sue has 15 cards as shown below:

T E L E V I S I O N C A L L S

Sue picks a card at random.
What is the probability that she picks the letter:

    a C   **b** E   **c** L   **d** S

2 Angus has a bag which contains 7 toffees, 4 mints and 2 chocolates. Angus picks one of these sweets. What is the probability that he chooses a:

a mint   **b** mint or toffee   **c** mint or chocolate

3 A bag contains 10 beads. There are 6 blue, 3 red and 1 green.

a Find the probability of selecting a red bead.

b 2 more blue beads are put in the bag.
Find the probability of selecting a blue bead.

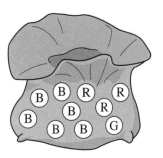

4 24 people come for a job interview. 9 of these people wear glasses and 4 of them have contact lenses.

Find the probability that the person chosen for the job:

a has contact lenses

b wears glasses

c does not wear glasses or contact lenses

5 Wendy has six £5 notes, ten £10 notes and four £20 notes in her purse. If she takes out one note, what is the probability that it will be:

a a £20 note   **b** a £5 or £10 note   **c** a £50 note

d She buys a new toaster with a £20 note and a £10 note. If she now took out a note, what is the probability that it would be a £10 note?

6 Reuben throws an 8-sided dice (faces numbered from 1 to 8) once. What is the probability of getting:

a a multiple of 2   **b** a prime number   **c** a factor of 8

7 One night a kennel has 16 dogs and 7 cats in its care. The following morning 3 dogs and 4 cats are picked up by their owners and 2 dogs are dropped off at the kennel.

Another owner arrives. What is the probability that if the owner has come to pick up one pet only, it will be a cat?

8 One ball is selected from a bag containing x red balls, y blue balls and z yellow balls. What is the probability of selecting a blue ball?

9 A box contains n beads. 8 beads are blue, m beads are green and the remaining beads are yellow. If one bead is removed, what is the probability that it will be yellow?

10 A bag contains x balls. y balls are removed and z balls are added. 6 balls are white. If one white ball is removed, what is the probability that the next ball to be removed will *not* be white?

TASK M8.3 ──────────────────────────────── **Main Book Page 236**

1 A coin is thrown 48 times. How many times would you expect it to land on 'heads'?

2 A dice is thrown 120 times. How many times would you expect to get a:
a 3   **b** 5   **c** 4 or 5   **d** square number

3 This spinner is spun 80 times.
How many times should the spinner land on a '0'?

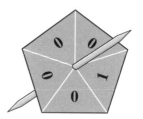

4 The probability of Canning Albion winning a football match is $\frac{2}{3}$.
If they play 42 matches in a season, how many matches are they likely to win?

5 The probability of Rob going to the pub on any one day is $\frac{2}{7}$.
How many times is he likely to go to the pub in the next fortnight?

6 A bag contains 5 blue balls, 4 red balls and 1 yellow ball.
Brenda takes out one ball at random and then puts it back.
If she does this 70 times, how many times should she take out:
a a yellow ball
b a blue ball
c a blue or red ball

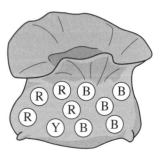

7 The probability of Manchester United winning the Premiership during a season is 0·17.
How many times are Manchester United likely to win the Premiership during the 21st century?

8 A bag has only red and blue discs in it. The probability of picking red is $\frac{2}{5}$.
a What is the probability of picking a blue disc?
b Sam picks out 4 red discs without replacing them. What is the smallest number of blue discs that could have been in the bag?
c If Sam picks out a total of 6 red discs without replacing them, what is the smallest number of blue discs that could have been in the bag?

TASK M8.4 ━━━━━━━━━━━━━━━━━━━━━━━━━━━━━━━━━ **Main Book Page 238**

1 Here are 2 spinners. If I spin both spinners, I could get a '1' and a '4' (1, 4).

 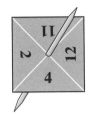

    a List *all* the possible outcomes.

    b How many possible outcomes are there?

2 Three babies are born. List *all* the boy/girl mixes (example: B G B boy, girl, boy).

3 Bart has 4 films (<u>A</u>ntz, <u>K</u>ing Kong, <u>J</u>ungle Book and The <u>T</u>erminator). He only has time to watch two of the films. List all the possible pairs of films that he could watch.

4 Nina has 2 spinners. She spins both spinners and multiplies the numbers. For example a '3' and a '4' give 12.

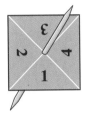 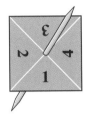

    a Copy and complete this grid to show *all* the possible outcomes.

Find the probability of getting a product which is:

    b an odd number

    c less than 3

    d a prime number

×	1	2	3	4
1				
2				
3				12
4				

5

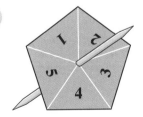

Marie and Don play a game involving a spinner and a dice.

Marie wins if the spinner gives a square number and the dice gives a multiple of 3.

Don wins if the spinner gives an even number and the dice gives a factor of 15.

Any other outcome is a draw.

Is this game fair to both players? Give reasons for your answer.

1 There is a row of 6 seats in a classroom. There are 6 students, Ashley, Leah, Arna, Dimitri, Tyler and Mark. The teacher tells Arna and Tyler that they must sit on the middle 2 seats. The other 4 students may sit on any of the other 4 seats.

In how many different ways can the 6 students seat themselves on the 6 seats?

2 | E | | a | | s | | y | | 1 |

A password requires 5 characters. The first character must be an upper case letter of the alphabet. The next 3 characters must each be a lower case letter of the alphabet. The final character must be a digit from 0 to 9. How many different passwords are possible?

3 Alex is 18 years old and was born on the 23rd January. His parents' birthdays are on the 2nd April and 15th May. Alex plays the National Lottery each week. He must choose six numbers from 1 to 49.

Each week he chooses his age and the birthday dates of his parents and himself.
He then randomly chooses two other numbers.

How many different sets of six Lottery numbers might he choose in any one week?

4 | 9 | | ? | | ? | | ? | | ? |

The digits 1 to 9 may each be used once only to make a five digit code. The code must be an odd number and begin with the digit 9. How many different codes are possible?

5 Cherie, Tom, Gabby, Pearl and Harry have 5 season tickets for their local football team. Their seats are in order from 237 to 241.

Cherie always sits in seat number 237. The others change around on their seats each time but Tom and Gabby always sit next to each other. In how many different ways might they be seated?

6 There are 15 runners in a 3000 m race.

a In how many different ways can the first 3 places be filled at the end of the race?
(Note – a different order is a different way)

b If the order does not matter, how many different groups of 3 runners can fill the first 3 places? (Hint – consider how many different ways that 3 items can be arranged)

7 | 1 | | 2 | | 3 | | 4 | | 5 | | 6 |

Each number above may be used once only. Show that the number of odd six-digit numbers greater than 500 000 that can be made is 120.

8 A History exam has 2 sections A and B. A candidate must attempt 2 questions from a possible 4 in section A and 2 questions from a possible 5 in section B.

How many different ways are there of selecting questions to complete this History exam?

TASK M8.5 ———————————————————————————— **Main Book Page 244**

1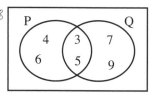

Find

a Q' **b** $P \cap Q$ **c** $n(P)$

d $P \cup Q'$ **e** $P' \cup Q'$ **f** $P' \cap Q$

2 $A = \{4, 5, 8, 9, 10\}$, $B = \{5, 9, 11, 12\}$ and $C = \{2, 3, 5, 9, 10, 11\}$

Find

a $B \cup C$ **b** $n(A \cap B)$ **c** $(A \cap B) \cup C$ **d** $A \cap B \cap C$

3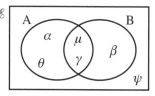

Find

a $(A \cup B)'$ **b** $A \cap B'$ **c** $n(A' \cap B)$

d $n(B')$ **e** $(A \cup B')'$ **f** $(A \cap B')'$

4 $M = \{x : x \text{ is a prime number}, 5 < x \le 12\}$ and $N = \{10, 11, 12, 13, 14\}$.

State which of the statements below are true.

a $M \cap N = \{11\}$ **b** $n(M \cup N) = 7$ **c** $7 \in M \cup N$

5 Find

a $A' \cup B$ **b** $n(A' \cap B)$ **c** A'

d $(A \cup B)'$ **e** $A \cup B'$ **f** $(A' \cap B)'$

g $n(A' \cup B)'$ **h** $(A \cup B')'$ **i** $(A' \cap B')'$

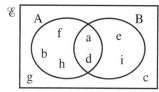

TASK M8.6 ———————————————————————————— **Main Book Page 245**

1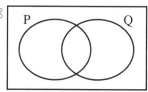

Draw 6 diagrams like the one shown opposite.
Shade each of the following sets.

a $(P \cup Q)'$ **b** $P' \cap Q$ **c** P'

d $(P \cap Q)'$ **e** $P \cup Q'$ **f** $(P' \cup Q)'$

2 Describe each shaded region.

a 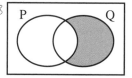 **b** 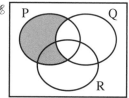 **c**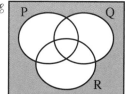

3 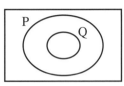 Copy the diagram opposite and shade P′ ∪ Q.

4 Draw 6 diagrams like the one shown opposite.
Shade each of the following sets.

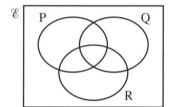

a P ∪ Q′   **b** P ∩ (Q ∪ R)

c (P ∩ Q′) ∩ R   **d** (P ∩ R) ∪ Q′

e P′ ∩ (Q′ ∩ R)   **f** (P ∩ Q ∩ R′)′

TASK M8.7 ———————————————————————— **Main Book Page 246**

1 The Venn diagram shows

ℰ = {people on a flight to Austria}

H = {people from Hatton}

S = {people going to ski}

ℰ
H   S
5 42 17
16

If one person is chosen at random then find

a p(person from Hatton)   **b** p(person who skis)

c p(person from Hatton who does not ski)   **d** p(person does not ski)

2 The Venn diagram shows

ℰ = {Year 11 students in Horton High School}

B = {Year 11 students who eat a school breakfast}

L = {Year 11 students who eat a school lunch}

ℰ
B   L
9 46 40
105

a Find p(B ∪ L)   **b** Find p(B′ ∩ L)

c Describe in words what p(B′ ∩ L) means.

d Find p(a student eats a school breakfast or school lunch but not both)

e Find p(B ∪ L′)

3 If p(A ∩ B′) = p(A ∩ B), find the value of p(B′).

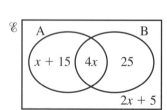

4 83 cars are examined for power steering (P), air conditioning (C) and automatic windows (W).
16 cars have power steering only, 10 have air conditioning only and 6 have automatic windows
only. 5 cars have P, C and W.

16 cars have P and W (no C), *x* cars have C and W (no P) and 2*x* cars have P and C (no W).

The same number of cars have no P, C or W as have P and C (no W).

If one car is chosen at random, find

a $p(P)$ **b** $p(C \cap W)$ **c** $p(C \cup W)$ **d** $p(C \cap P')$

e How many cars have no P, C or W?

5 75 people attend a Music course. 28 of them play the piano and 40 of them play the guitar. 11 of them play both the piano and the guitar. If one of these people is chosen at random, find the probability that this person does not play the piano or the guitar.

TASK M8.8   **Main Book Page 248**

1 A coin is thrown twice. What is the probability of getting 2 heads?

2 A dice is thrown twice. What is the probability of getting a '3' *followed* by a '4'?

3 A card is chosen from a pack of 52 playing cards then replaced. Another card is chosen. What is the probability of obtaining:

a 2 diamond cards?   **b** 2 aces?

4 A bag contains 6 yellow beads, 3 blue beads and 2 green beads.

I remove one bead at random, replace it then take another bead.

What is the probability that:

a both beads are blue?

b both beads are green?

5 The probability that Will takes an umbrella to work is 0·4.

The probability that it rains is 0·7.

What is the probability that:

a Will takes his umbrella and it rains?

b Will does *not* take his umbrella and it rains?

c Will does *not* take his umbrella and it does *not* rain?

6 2 darts are thrown at this board.

Assuming each dart hits the board, what is the probability that:

a both darts hit an even number?

b both darts hit a square number?

c both darts hit a prime number?

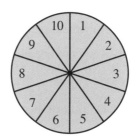

7 If a dice is thrown four times, what is the probability of obtaining four sixes?

8 The probability that Serena works on a Saturday is $\frac{3}{4}$. The probability that she goes to a night club on a Saturday evening is $\frac{4}{7}$.

On any Saturday what is the probability that:

a Serena does *not* work but goes to a night club?

b Serena works and goes to a night club?

TASK M8.9 ——————————————————————— **Main Book Page 250**

1 The players in an amateur football team have the jobs shown below:

Team position	Job
goalkeeper	plumber
defenders	teacher, farmer, mechanic, artist
midfielders	farmer, fireman, insurance salesman
forwards	electrician, teacher, bus driver

Which of the following pairs are mutually exclusive?

a a teacher and a midfielder

b a farmer and a defender

c an electrician and a forward

2 The probability of Karen playing certain sports is shown in the table below.

Hockey	Football	Badminton	Netball
0·5	0·1	x	0·2

a What is the probability of Karen playing hockey or netball?

b What is the probability of Karen playing badminton?

3 The probability of the next person walking into the room being a woman is $\frac{1}{3}$.

The probability of the next person walking into the room wearing glasses is $\frac{1}{10}$.

The probability of the next person walking into the room being a woman and wearing glasses is $\frac{1}{30}$.

Work out the probability of the next person walking into the room being a woman or wearing glasses.

4 A bag contains 6 blue beads numbered 1 to 6.

It also contains 6 yellow beads numbered 1 to 6.

If one bead is randomly removed, what is the probability of taking a blue bead or a bead with the number 6 on it?

5 Dan gets to work by either car, bus, tube or bike. The table shows the probability of each being used.

Car	Bus	Tube	Bike
0·25		0·4	0·2

a What is the probability of Dan going to work by bus.

b What is the probability of Dan going to work by car or bus.

c On his 20 working days in March, how many days would you expect Dan to take the tube?

6 There are 4 people in a car. One person is wearing glasses. 2 people are wearing hats.

Explain why the probability of a person in the car wearing glasses or a hat is *not* necessarily $\frac{3}{4}$.

7 John has some coins in his pocket. He has £1, £2 and 50p coins. The probability of choosing a £1 coin is 0·65. The probability of choosing a £2 coin is 0·2.

a What is the probability of choosing a 50p coin?

b What is the probability of choosing a £2 coin or a 50p coin?

8 A dartboard has 20 sectors. Half the sectors are red and half are yellow. The red sectors have the odd numbers 1 to 19 and the yellow sectors have the even numbers 2 to 20.

A dart can land randomly on any sector. What is the probability that the dart will land on a yellow sector or a sector with a multiple of 3?

TASK M8.10   **Main Book Page 253**

1 A bag contains 8 blue discs and 3 green discs.

One disc is removed at random then replaced.

Another disc is then removed.

a Copy and complete the tree diagram to show all the outcomes.

Find the probability that:

b both discs are blue

c both discs are green

d one disc is blue and one disc is green (in any order)

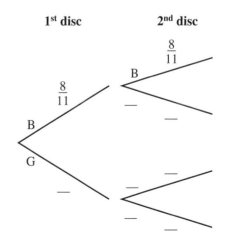

2 The probability of Jack swimming on any one day is 0·3.

a Copy and complete the tree diagram showing whether he swims or not on a Thursday and Friday.

b Find the probability that:
   i Jack does *not* swim on either day
   ii Jack swims on one day *only*

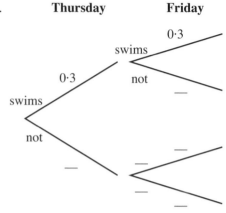

3 A spinner is spun three times.

a Copy and complete the tree diagram to show the probability of getting a 'two'.

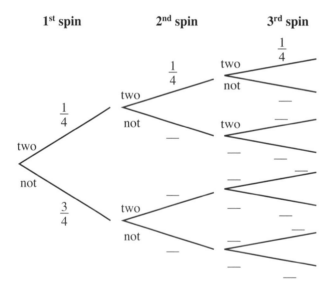

b Find the probability that the spinner lands on:
   i 3 two's   **ii** no two's   **iii** *at least* one 'two'

4 A dice is thrown three times. Find the probability that the dice lands on:

a exactly two 3's   **b** *at least* one 3

5 The probability of Stacey eating a curry on any day is 0·2.

Draw a tree diagram to help you find the probability that on a Friday, Saturday and Sunday:

a Stacey has a curry each day

b Stacey has a curry on exactly one day only

a Stacey has a curry on *at least* one day

TASK M8.11 ──────────────────────────── **Main Book Page 257**

1 There are 3 males and 5 females in a family of 8 people.
Two of the family members are chosen at random.

a Copy and complete the tree diagram.

Find the probability that:

b both people are female

c exactly one person is female

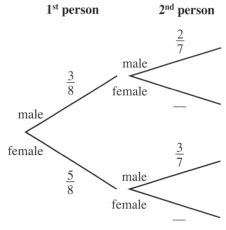

2 Charlie has 7 creme eggs and 2 caramel eggs. He eats 2 eggs randomly.

a Draw a tree diagram to show all outcomes.

Find the probability that:

b Charlie eats 2 creme eggs

c Charlie eats one creme egg and one caramel egg

d Charlie eats 2 eggs of the same type

3 Three cards are taken at random from
a pack of 52 cards.

a Copy and complete the tree diagram.

b Find the probability that:
   i all 3 cards are clubs
   ii *at least* one card is a club
   iii exactly one card is a club

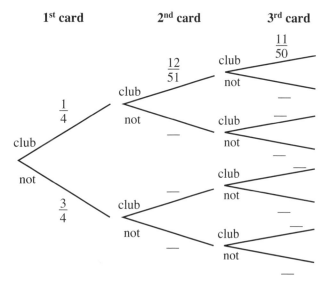

4 There are 12 beads in a bag. 5 beads are red and the rest are blue. Three beads are taken out at random, one at a time, without replacement.

a Draw a tree to show all outcomes.

Find the probability that:

b all three beads are blue

c *at least* one bead is red

d exactly one bead is blue and two beads are red

5 A box contains 15 counters, x counters are red and the remainder are blue. Two counters are removed at random. What is the probability, in terms of x, of removing:

a two blue counters?

b *at least* one blue counter?

c one counter of each colour?

TASK E8.2 ——————————————————————— **Main Book Page 260**

1 65% of properties for sale in a town are over-priced. If a property is over-priced, the probability of getting the asking price is 0.3. If the property is not over-priced, the probability of getting the asking price is 0.85.

a Draw a tree diagram to represent the above information.

b Find the probability of not receiving the asking price.

c Given that the asking price is received, find the probability that the property is not over-priced (give the answer to 3 decimal places).

2 28 students attend football and rugby practices. The Venn diagram shows how many students are in the football team (F) and the rugby team (R).

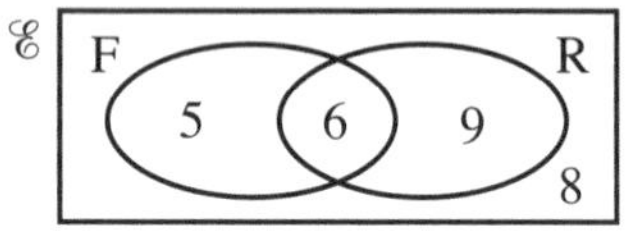

One of the students is chosen at random.

a Find the probability that the student plays for the rugby team but not the football team.

b Given that the student plays for the football team, find the probability that the student also plays for the rugby team.

3 Some people are asked who they would vote for at the next election. The table below shows this information.

	Labour	Conservative	Lib Democrats	Green Party
male	62	60	28	16
female	49	71	46	15

Find the probability (to 3 decimal places) that one of these people, chosen at random,

a would vote for the Green Party

b would vote Labour given that the person is male

c is female given that the person voted for the Conservatives

4 The frequency tree shows a group of 100 people and whether they are 65 years old or over and whether they drive.

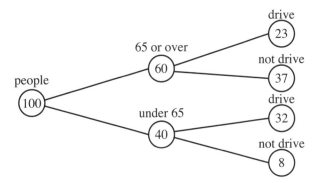

a What is the probability that a person chosen at random drives?

b Given that a person does not drive, what is the probability that this person is under 65?

5 The probability of Amy doing more than 2 hours homework on a Thursday evening is 0·6. If she does more than 2 hours homework, the probability of seeing friends later that evening is 0·25. If she does 2 hours or less homework, the probability of seeing friends later that evening is 0·7.

a Find the probability that Amy will see friends later that evening.

b Given that Amy does not see her friends later that evening, find the probability that she did more than 2 hours homework (give the answer to 3 decimal places).

6 96 people are asked if they rent or not. Some of the people live in Denton.

R = {people who rent}

D = {people who live in Denton}

A person is chosen at random. Find the probability that this person rents given that the person lives in Denton.

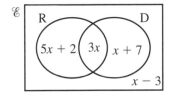

| TASK E8.3 | Main Book Page 263 |

1 The probability of a garden gate being left open is 0·15. If the gate is left open, the probability of a dog getting out of the garden is 0·8. If the gate is shut, the probability of the dog getting out of the garden is 0·3.

a Copy and complete the tree diagram.

b Find the probability that the dog gets out of the garden.

c Given that the dog does not get out of the garden, find the probability that the gate was left open (give the answer to 3 decimal places).

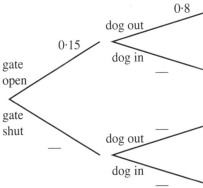

2 Some people are asked whether during one week they had a pizza (P), an indian meal (I) or a chinese meal (C).

   7 people said they had all 3.
    8 people said they had P and I (no C).
  12 people said they had I and C (no P).
  14 people said they had P and C (no I).
  16 people said they had P only.
  25 people said they had I only.
  23 people said they had C only.
  42 people had none of this food.

One of the people is selected at random. Find

a $p(I)$ **b** $p(C \cap P)$ **c** $p(I \cap C')$

d $p(I \cap P \cap C)$ **e** $p(P$ given $C)$ **f** $p(I$ given $P')$

g Describe in words exactly what is meant by $p(I \cap C')$.

3 A rugby team plays 40% of its matches at home. They win 75% of their home matches but only 55% of their away matches.

a Draw a tree diagram to represent the above information.

b Find the probability that the team wins a match.

c Find the probability that the team is playing away given that the team loses the match (give the answer to 3 decimal places).

4 If a car salesperson sells more than 3 cars during the week, the probability of taking the next weekend off is $\frac{7}{8}$. If 3 or less cars are sold during the week, the probability of taking the next weekend off is $\frac{2}{5}$. If the probability of selling more than 3 cars during the week is $\frac{1}{5}$, find the probability that the car salesperson will take the next weekend off.

5 The frequency tree shows 160 washing machines and whether they are 3 years old or more and whether they develop a fault during the current year.

a Find the probability that a washing machine chosen at random developed a fault during the current year.

b Given that a washing machine is 3 years old or more, what is the probability that it has not developed a fault during the current year?

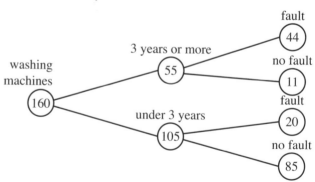

6 A bag contains n counters. Seven of these counters are green and the rest are yellow. Two counters are chosen at random. The probability that the two counters are green is $\frac{1}{5}$.

   a Form an equation involving n and show that it simplifies to $n^2 - n - 210 = 0$.

   b Find how many counters were in the bag originally.

7 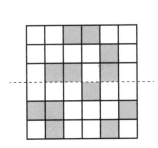 The Venn diagram shows how many students in a school study Geography (G) or History (H) in Year 11 in Hatton High School.

There are 88 students in total. The same number of students study Geography only as study History only. If one student is chosen at random, find the probability that

   a the student studies Geography and History.

   b the student studies Geography given that he/she does *not* study History.

GEOMETRY 2   9

TASK M9.1   **Main Book Page 275**

1 Copy the patterns below on squared paper. Shade in as many squares as necessary to complete the symmetrical patterns. The dotted lines are lines of symmetry.

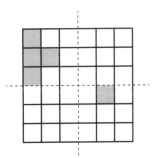

2 Sketch these shapes in your book and draw on *all* the *lines of symmetry*.

  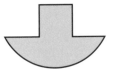

For each shape write the *order* of *rotational symmetry* (you may use tracing paper).

3  **4**   **5** 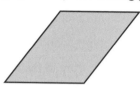 **6**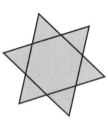

7  **8**  **9** 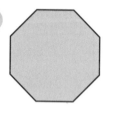 **10**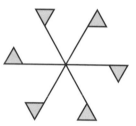

11 Draw your own shape which has an order of rotational symmetry of 3.

12 Draw a triangle which has *no* rotational symmetry.

TASK M9.2 ━━━━━━━━━━━━━━━━━━━━━━━━━━━━━━ **Main Book Page 276**

1 How many planes of symmetry does this triangular prism have?

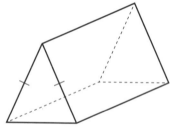

2 Draw each shape below and show one plane of symmetry.

a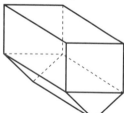

b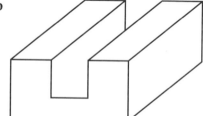

c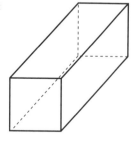

d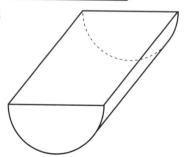

3 How many planes of symmetry does a cube have?

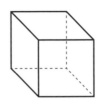

TASK M9.3 ──────────────────────────── **Main Book Page 278**

1 Use translation vectors to describe the following translations.

a D to C	**b** E to D
c A to B	**d** E to F
e D to H	**f** H to F
g E to B	**h** E to G
i G to D	**j** F to C

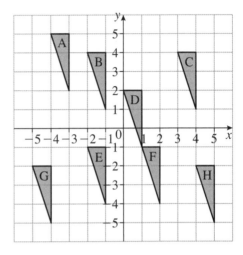

2 Copy the grid opposite and draw shape A as shown. Translate shape A by each of the translation vectors shown below:

a $\begin{pmatrix} -4 \\ 1 \end{pmatrix}$ Label new shape B.

b $\begin{pmatrix} 1 \\ -3 \end{pmatrix}$ Label new shape C.

c $\begin{pmatrix} -4 \\ -3 \end{pmatrix}$ Label new shape D.

d $\begin{pmatrix} -1 \\ -5 \end{pmatrix}$ Label new shape E.

e Use a translation vector to describe the translation that moves shape D to E.

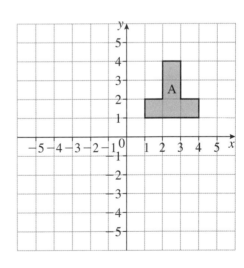

96

1 For each pair of shapes below, write down the equation of the *line of reflection*.

  a A to B

  b A to C

  c C to D

  d D to E

  e E to F

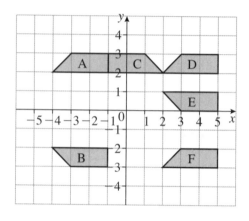

2 Copy the grid and shape opposite.

  a Reflect rectangle A in the line $y = x - 1$. Label the image B.

  b Draw the line $y = -x$.

  c Reflect rectangle A in the line $y = -x$. Label the image C.

  d Write down the translation vector which transforms rectangle C onto rectangle B.

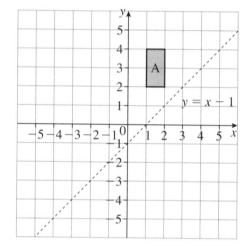

3 **a** Draw an x-axis from -4 to 6 and y-axis from -4 to 6.

  b Draw a triangle P with vertices (1, 3), (1, 6) and (2, 3).

  c Reflect triangle P in the line $y = x$. Label the image Q.

  d Reflect triangle Q in the line $x + y = 3$. Label the image R.

  e Reflect triangle R in the line $x = -1$. Label the image S.

  f Reflect triangle S in the x-axis. Label the image T.

  g Describe fully the transformation which maps T back onto P.

4 **a** Draw an x-axis from -5 to 5 and a y-axis from -5 to 5.

  b Draw an ⌐-shape A with vertices $(-2, 1)$, $(-2, 4)$, $(-4, 4)$, $(-4, 3)$, $(-3, 3)$ and $(-3, 1)$.

  c Translate shape A through $\begin{pmatrix} 3 \\ 0 \end{pmatrix}$. Label the image B.

  d Reflect shape B in the line $y = x$. Label the image C.

  e Translate shape C through $\begin{pmatrix} -1 \\ -2 \end{pmatrix}$. Label the image D.

  f Shape D is reflected back onto shape A. Write down the equation of the *line of reflection*.

You may use tracing paper.

For each question, draw the shape and the centre of rotation (C). Rotate the shape as indicated and draw the image.

1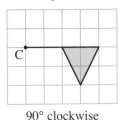

90° clockwise

2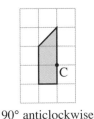

90° anticlockwise

3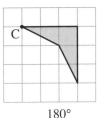

180°

4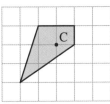

90° anticlockwise

5 Find the co-ordinates of the centres of the following rotations:

a shape A onto shape B

b shape B onto shape C

c shape C onto shape D

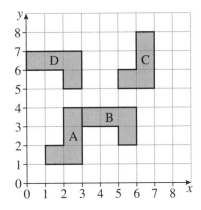

6 a Draw the *x* axis from −6 to 5.
Draw the *y* axis from −6 to 7.
Draw rectangle A with vertices at (2, −2), (3, −2), (3, −5), (2, −5).

b Rotate rectangle A 90° clockwise about (2, −1). Label the image B.

c Rotate rectangle B 90° clockwise about (−2, −2). Label the image C.

d Rotate rectangle C 90° clockwise about the origin. Label the image D.

e Rotate rectangle D 90° anticlockwise about (−2, 2). Label the image E.

f Describe *fully* the *translation* which transforms rectangle A onto rectangle E.

7 Describe *fully* the rotation which transforms:

a triangle A onto triangle B

b triangle C onto triangle D

c triangle B onto triangle C

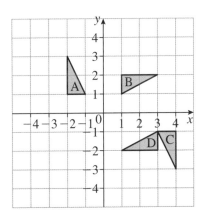

98

For questions **1** and **2**, draw the grid and the 2 shapes then draw broken lines through pairs of points in the new shape and the old shape. Describe *fully* the enlargement which transforms shape A onto shape B.

1

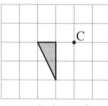

2

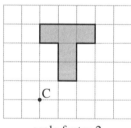

For questions **3** to **5**, copy the diagram and then draw an enlargement using the scale factor and centre of enlargement (C) given. Leave room for the enlargement!

3

scale factor 3

4

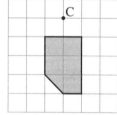

scale factor 2

5

scale factor 2

6 **a** Draw an x-axis from -7 to 7 and a y-axis from -7 to 7.

b Draw a rectangle P with vertices at $(-1, -2)$, $(-1, -3)$, $(-3, -3)$ and $(-3, -2)$.

c Enlarge rectangle P by scale factor 2 about $(0, 0)$. Label the image Q.

d Translate rectangle Q through $\binom{8}{3}$. Label the image R.

e Enlarge rectangle R by scale factor 2 about $(6, -7)$. Label the image S.

f Enlarge rectangle S by scale factor $\frac{1}{4}$ about $(-6, 5)$. Label the image T.

g Describe fully the transformation which maps T onto P.

1 **a** Draw an *x*-axis from −5 to 5 and a *y*-axis from −5 to 5.

   b Draw an ⌐-shape with vertices (−4, 2), (−4, 3), (−3, 3), (−3, 4), (−5, 4) and (−5, 2).

   c Enlarge the shape by a scale factor of −2 about (−2, 1).

   d If P is the vertex (−5, 2) in the original shape, write down the co-ordinates of the corresponding vertex in the new shape.

For questions **2** and **3**, describe fully the enlargement which transforms shape A onto shape B (draw the grid and shape if necessary).

2
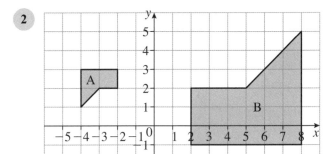

3
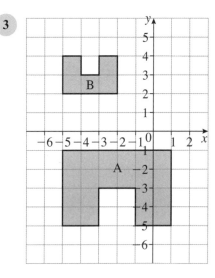

4 **a** Draw an *x*-axis from −6 to 4 and a *y*-axis from −10 to 4.

   b Draw a triangle A with vertices at (1, 1), (1, 3) and (2, 1).

   c Enlarge triangle A by a scale factor of −3 about the origin. Label the image B.

   d Enlarge triangle B by a scale factor of $-\frac{1}{3}$ about (0, −3). Label the image C.

   e Describe fully the transformation which maps C onto A.

100

1 Describe *fully* the transformation which moves:

   a triangle A onto triangle B

   b triangle B onto triangle C

   c triangle C onto triangle D

   d triangle D onto triangle E

   e triangle D onto triangle F

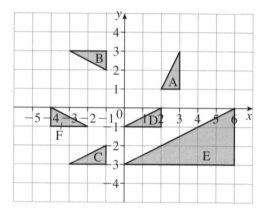

2 **a** Draw the x-axis from -5 to 5.
Draw the y-axis from -6 to 6.
Draw shape A with vertices at $(-2, 2)$, $(-4, 2)$, $(-4, 4)$, $(-2, 6)$.

   b Enlarge shape A by scale factor $\frac{1}{2}$ about the origin. Label the image B.

   c Reflect shape B in the line $y = -1$. Label the image C.

   d Rotate shape C 90° anticlockwise about $(-2, -2)$. Label the image D.

   e Translate shape D through $\binom{3}{4}$. Label the image E.

   f Rotate shape E 90° clockwise about $(2, 2)$. Label the image F.

   f Describe *fully* the transformation that would move shape F onto shape C.

3 **a** Draw an x-axis from -7 to 7 and a y-axis from -7 to 7.

   b Draw rectangle P with vertices at $(-4, -2)$, $(-4, -6)$, $(-6, -6)$ and $(-6, -2)$.

   c Enlarge rectangle P by a scale factor of $-\frac{1}{2}$ about the origin. Label the image Q.

   d Reflect rectangle Q in the line $x + y = 6$. Label the image R.

   e Rotate rectangle R 90° clockwise about the origin. Label the image S.

   f Translate rectangle S through $\binom{-10}{6}$. Label the image T.

   g Describe fully the transformation which maps T onto Q.

1 *Explain* why these two triangles are congruent.

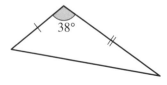

2 *Explain* why these two triangles are *not* congruent.

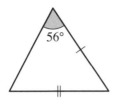 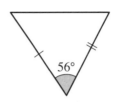

3 AB is parallel to DE.

BC = CD.

Prove that triangles ABC and CDE are congruent.

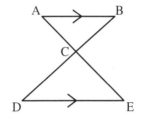

4 **a** Prove that triangles ACX and ACY are congruent.

  b *Explain* why AY = CX.

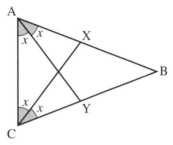

5 ABCD is a parallelogram.

Prove that triangles ABD and CBD are congruent.

6 PR = RS.

Prove that triangles PQR and RTS are congruent.

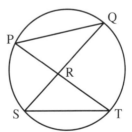

7 Triangle BCE is isosceles as shown.

AB = ED.

  a Prove that triangles ABC and CED are congruent.

  b *Explain* why BÂC = CD̂E.

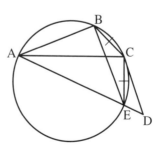

8 PQRS is a kite.

Use congruent triangles to prove that diagonal PR bisects $S\hat{P}Q$.

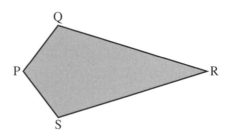

9

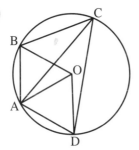

O is the centre of the circle.

AC bisects $B\hat{C}D$.

Prove that triangles ABO and DAO are congruent.

10 Triangle ABC is isosceles with AB = BC.

M and N are the midpoints of AB and BC respectively.

PQBM and BRSN are both squares.

a Prove that triangles BRM and BNQ are congruent.

b Explain why MR = NQ.

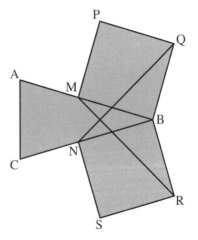

GEOMETRY 3   10

| **TASK M10.1** | **Main Book Page 306** |

1 A shop uses 40 g of cheese in one sandwich. How many sandwiches will the shop make if it has 3·2 kg of cheese?

2 Ninety-two 330 ml bottles of coke are sold at a fête.
How many litres is this in total?

3 Copy and complete the following:

a 2·6 m = ☐ cm   b 3·82 m = ☐ cm   c 470 cm = ☐ m

d 90 mm = ☐ cm   e 4 mm = ☐ cm   f 1500 m = ☐ km

g 3·5 kg = ☐ g   h 600 g = ☐ kg   i 0·28 kg = ☐ g

j 1·9 tonnes = ☐ kg   k 620 ml = ☐ litre   l 1937 litres = ☐ ml

m 8·2 litres = ☐ ml   n 3·26 litres = ☐ ml   o 43 g = ☐ kg

4 Karli says that a medicine spoon can hold 0·5 litres of medicine. Is she correct?
Justify your answer.

5 Kevin uses 220 g butter in each cake he makes. He has 14 kg butter available.
He needs to make 65 cakes. Has he got enough butter?
Show your working out clearly.

6 Write the following amounts in order of size, starting with the smallest.

a 8 cm,   0·81 m,   7·4 cm,   83 mm

b 780 g,   0·7 kg,   738 g,   0·79 kg

c 5 km,   57 m,   509 m,   0·6 km,   4·7 km

d 274 ml,   0·28 litres,   0·279 litres,   275 ml,   2·14 litres

---

TASK M10.2 ───────────────────────────── **Main Book Page 308**

> **Remember:** 1 inch ≈ 2·5 cm   1 ounce ≈ 30 g   1 litre ≈ 1·8 pints
>   1 foot ≈ 30 cm   1 kg ≈ 2·2 pounds   1 gallon ≈ 4·5 litres
>   1 yard ≈ 90 cm
>   1 mile ≈ 1·6 km

1 Copy and complete:

a 10 gallons ≈ ☐ litres   b 20 kg ≈ ☐ pounds

c 4 gallons ≈ ☐ litres   d 6 inches ≈ ☐ cm

e 10 miles ≈ ☐ km   f $2\frac{1}{2}$ feet ≈ ☐ cm

g 180 ounces ≈ ☐ g   h 27 litres ≈ ☐ gallons

i 17·5 cm ≈ ☐ inches   j $3\frac{1}{2}$ yards ≈ ☐ cm

2 Which imperial unit would you use to measure:

a the mass of a man   b the length of a book   c the height of a house

3 Harry cycles 20 miles. Louise cycles 30 km. Who cycles further?

4 Tom needs 6·5 pounds of flour. If he buys a 2 kg bag of flour and a 1 kg bag of flour,
will he have enough flour? Explain your answer fully.

5

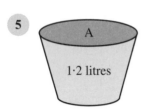

1·2 litres

If each container is filled up with water, which container will hold the most?

2·2 pints

6 Which amount is the smaller?

    a 3 gallons or 14 litres?   **b** 8 miles or 12 km?

    c 5 km or 3 miles?   **d** 5 kg or 10 pounds?

    e 8 yards or 700 cm?   **f** 35 litres or 8 gallons?

    g 9 inches or 23 cm?   **h** 4 feet or 1 m?

7 The speed limit on the motorway is 70 miles per hour.
Anna, is travelling at 110 km per hour. Is she breaking the speed limit?
Explain your answer fully.

TASK M10.3 ——————————————————————— **Main Book Page 310**

Use $\triangle$ D / S | T to help you work out the questions below.

1 A train travels 504 km in 4 hours. What was the average speed of the train?

2 A coach covers a distance of $225\frac{1}{2}$ km at an average speed of 73 km/hr.
How long was the coach travelling for?

3 Jack cycles 3 km in 15 minutes. What was his average speed in km/hr?

4 Brenda drives from Nottingham to Leeds at an average speed of 84 km/hr.
The journey takes 1 hour 30 minutes. How far is it from Nottingham to Leeds?

5 A train travels 47 km in 20 minutes. What is the speed of the train in km/hr?

6 Connor walks $2\frac{1}{2}$ miles in $1\frac{1}{3}$ hours. Find his average speed in mph.

7 Alexis travels for 1 hour 12 minutes at a speed of 42 mph. How far does Alexis travel in this time?

8 Ellen drives 24 km from her home to work. She travels at an average speed of 32 km/hr.
If she leaves home at 8:05 a.m., when will she arrive at work?

9 Distance from Leeds (miles)

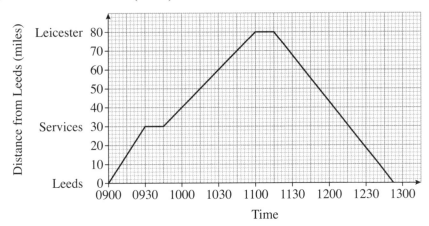

The graph above shows a car journey from Leeds to Leicester and back.

a How far from Leeds is the car at 1015?

b How far from Leeds is the car at 1036?

c Find the speed of the car between the Services and Leicester.

d On the return journey, at what time was the car 70 miles from Leeds?

e For how long did the car stop in Leicester?

f Find the speed of the car on the return journey from Leicester to Leeds.

10 Terry is travelling at 13 km/hr. Joel is moving at 3·5 m/s. Who is travelling faster?

11 A car travels at x m/s. Write down an expression for this speed in km/hr.

12 A train travels 253 km at an average speed of 92 km/hr then 45 km at an average speed of 10 m/s. Find the average speed for the whole journey in km/hr.

13 A cyclist travels at $3y$ km/hr. A car travels at $5x$ km/hr.
Find an expression for the difference in the speeds of the car and cyclist in m/s.

14 Arlene travels for 48 minutes at 75 km/hr then for 1 hour 12 minutes at x km/hr.
If she travels a total distance of 126 km, find the value of x.

| **TASK M10.4** | **Main Book Page 313** |

Use and ⟨F P A⟩ if necessary in the questions below.

1 A solid weighs 450 g and has a volume of 50 cm³. Find the density of this solid.

2 A liquid has a density of 2 g/cm³. How much does the liquid weigh if its volume is 240 cm³?

3 A metal bar has a density of 12 g/cm³ and a mass of 360 g. Find the volume of the metal bar.

4 A force of 42 N acts over an area of 8 m². Find the pressure.

5 A box weighs 160 N and exerts a pressure of 50 Pa on the floor. What is the area of the base of the box?

6 Which has a greater volume – 102·6 g of lead with density 11·4 g/cm³ or 78·85 g of steel with density 8·3 g/cm³? Write down by how much.

7 The density of this metal bar is 7·4 g/cm³.
Find the mass of this metal bar. Give your answer in kg.
(Note the length is given in metres.)

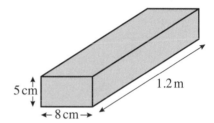

8

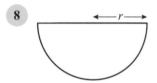

The base of a table leg is a semi-circle.
A force of 20 N acts through the leg
creating a pressure of 8000 Pa.
Calculate the radius of the semi-circle.

9 A metal cube of length 0·2 m has a density of 8·3 g/cm³. A hole is bored through the cube with 485 cm³ of metal being removed. What is the mass in kg of the remaining piece of metal?

10 A metal bar has 3 holes cut completely through its length. The cross-sectional area of each hole is y cm². The density of the metal is 9 g/cm³.
Find the mass of the remaining piece of metal, giving your answer in terms of x and y.

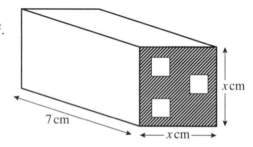

11 A cuboid has a mass of 6 kg which provides a weight of 60 N. The dimensions are 50 cm by 30 cm by 20 cm. On which face would the cuboid be standing if the greatest possible pressure were to be exerted on the ground? Explain your answer fully.

12 Metal A has density x g/cm³ and metal B has density y g/cm³.
m kg of metal A is mixed with n g of metal B to make an alloy. Find an expression in terms of m, n, x and y for the density of this alloy.

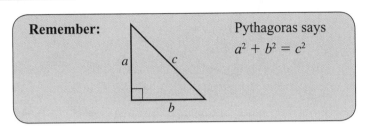

Remember: Pythagoras says
$$a^2 + b^2 = c^2$$

You will need a calculator. Give your answers correct to 2 decimal places where necessary. The units are cm.

1 Find the length AB.

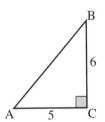

2 Find the length KL.

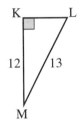

3 Find the length x.

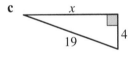

4 Find the length QR.

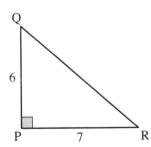

5 Find the length BC.

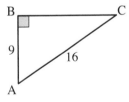

108

6 Calculate the length AB opposite.

7 Calculate the length of the line joining (1, 3) to (4, 7).

8 A triangle has vertices P(4, 5), Q(6, 9) and R(9, 1). Calculate the perimeter of triangle PQR.

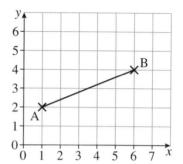

TASK M10.6 ———————————————————————— **Main Book Page 317**

You may use a calculator. Give answers to 2 decimal places.

1 A rectangle has length 9 cm and width 7 cm. Calculate the length of its diagonal.

2 Calculate the perimeter of this triangle.

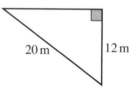

3 A ladder of length 7·5 m reaches 5·5 m up a vertical wall. How far is the foot of the ladder from the wall?

4 A plane flies 100 km due south and then a further 150 km due east. How far is the plane from its starting point?

5 Calculate the area of this triangle.

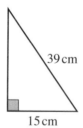

6 Find the 'exact' value of x for each triangle below.

a

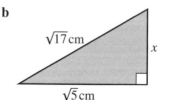

b **c**

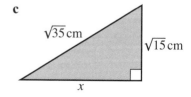

7 Find x.

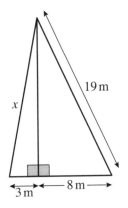

19 m

x

3 m ← 8 m →

8 Calculate the 'exact' length of the line joining $(2, 1)$ to $(4, 7)$.

9 Calculate the 'exact' length of the line joining $(4, -1)$ to $(1, 8)$.

10 Find the height of each isosceles triangle below:

a

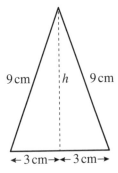

9 cm h 9 cm

← 3 cm →← 3 cm →

b

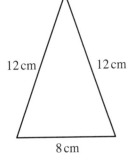

12 cm 12 cm

8 cm

11 Find the area of this isosceles triangle.

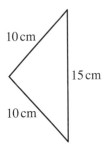

10 cm

15 cm

10 cm

12 Find the 'exact' perimeter of this trapezium.

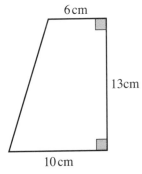

6 cm

13 cm

10 cm

110

In each triangle below, note the angle given and state whether the
identified side is in the correct position or not.

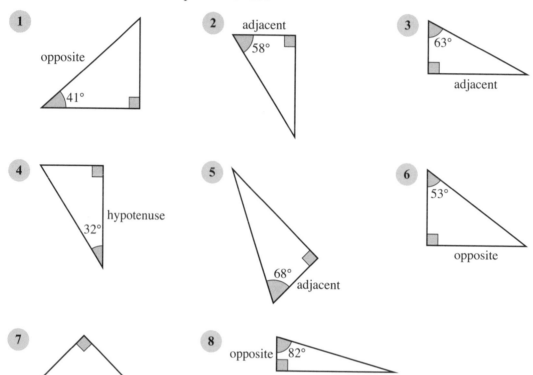

In each triangle below, find the sides marked with letters, correct to
3 significant figures. All lengths are in cm.

1 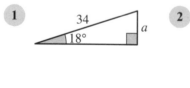 **2** 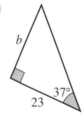 **3** 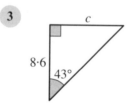 **4**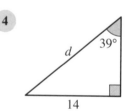

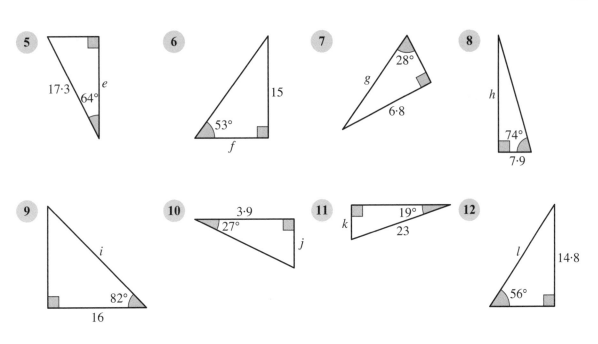

5 17·3 64° *e*

6 15 53° *f*

7 28° *g* 6·8

8 *h* 74° 7·9

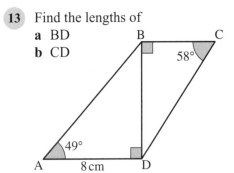

9 *i* 82° 16

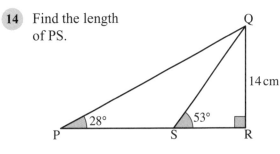

10 3·9 27° *j*

11 *k* 19° 23

12 *l* 14·8 56°

13 Find the lengths of
  a BD
  b CD

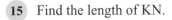

B C 58° A 49° 8 cm D

14 Find the length of PS.

Q 14 cm P 28° S 53° R

15 Find the length of KN.

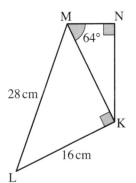

M N 64° 28 cm K 16 cm L

16 Find the length of TU.

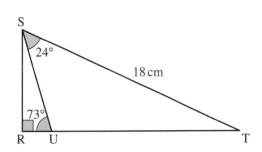

S 24° 18 cm 73° R U T

For each triangle below, find the angles marked, correct to one decimal place.
All lengths are in cm.

1
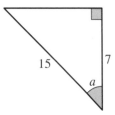

2
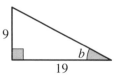

3
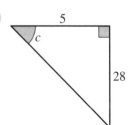

4
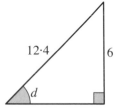

5
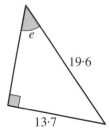

6
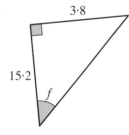

7
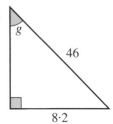

8
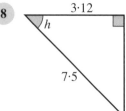

9 Find RŜP.

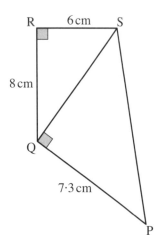

10 Find AD̂B.

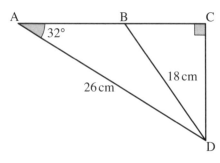

11 Find AB̂C.

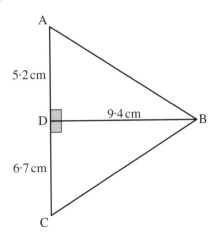

12 If PS : SR = 2 : 5, find SQ̂R.

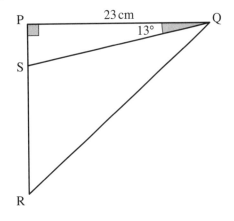

| **TASK M10.10** | **Main Book Page 326** |

Remember: $\sin 45° = \dfrac{1}{\sqrt{2}}$ or $\left(\dfrac{\sqrt{2}}{2}\right)$ $\qquad \sin 30° = \dfrac{1}{2} \qquad\qquad \sin 60° = \dfrac{\sqrt{3}}{2}$

$\cos 45° = \dfrac{1}{\sqrt{2}}$ or $\left(\dfrac{\sqrt{2}}{2}\right)$ $\qquad \cos 30° = \dfrac{\sqrt{3}}{2} \qquad\quad \cos 60° = \dfrac{1}{2}$

$\tan 45° = 1 \qquad\qquad\qquad\qquad \tan 30° = \dfrac{1}{\sqrt{3}}$ or $\left(\dfrac{\sqrt{3}}{3}\right) \qquad \tan 60° = \sqrt{3}$

For each triangle below, find the 'exact' value of x.
All lengths are in cm.

1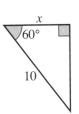

2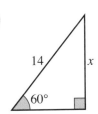

3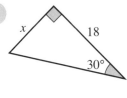

4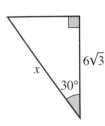

5 Find the 'exact' perimeter of each triangle.

a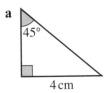

b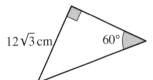

c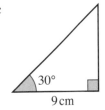

114

6

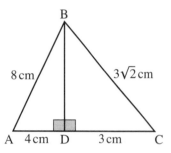

Find the value of AB̂C.

7

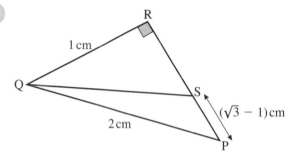

Find the value of PQ̂S.

8

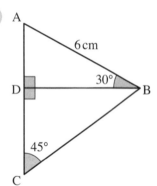

Prove that the area of
triangle ABC is $\frac{9}{2}(3 + \sqrt{3})$ cm².

TASK M10.11 ———————————————————— **Main Book Page 327**

In this Exercise give each answer to 3 significant figures or 1 decimal place for angles.

1 Find AB̂C.

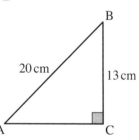

2 Find PR.

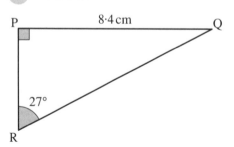

3 Find LM.

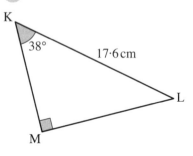

4 A builder wants a metal support to be inclined at an angle of 40° to the horizontal.
If the vertical height from the bottom to the top of the support is 3·8 m, what is the length of the metal support?

5 Find the length of PQ.

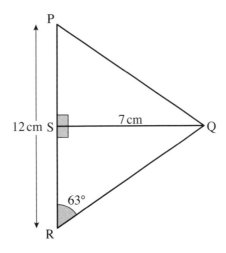

6 Work out the 'exact' perimeter of triangle ABC.

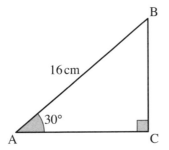

7 AC = BC and MC = 7 cm.
Find the area of triangle ABC.

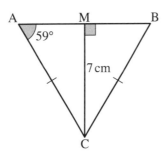

8 O is the centre of a circle of radius 6 cm.
If AÔB = 50°, find the area of triangle AOB.

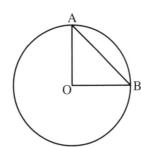

9 PQRS is a kite.
Find the length of PS.

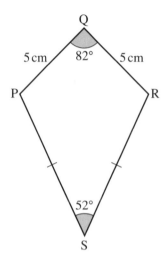

10

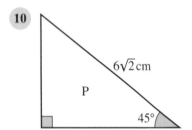

Which triangle has
the larger area and
by how much?

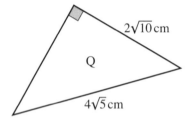

11 Find the length of AD.

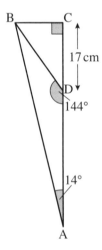

12 *Do not use a calculator in this question.*
O is the centre of the circle.
AC is a tangent to the circle.

$$\cos O\hat{A}B = \frac{12}{13}$$

$$\sin O\hat{A}B = \frac{5}{13}$$

$$\tan O\hat{A}B = \frac{5}{12}$$

Find the length of AD.

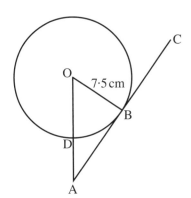

| **TASK M10.12** | **Main Book Page 333** |

1 Write each vector as a column vector, eg. $\overrightarrow{CD} = \begin{pmatrix} 1 \\ -1 \end{pmatrix}$

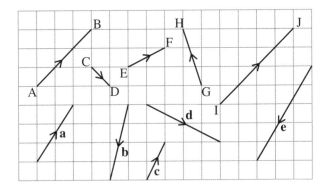

2 Calculate the length (modulus) of **a**, **b**, **c**, **d** and **e** in question **1**, leaving your answers in surd form.

3 Draw and label each vector below on squared paper.

$$f = \begin{pmatrix} 4 \\ -1 \end{pmatrix} \qquad g = \begin{pmatrix} 2 \\ 2 \end{pmatrix} \qquad h = \begin{pmatrix} -3 \\ -2 \end{pmatrix} \qquad \overrightarrow{PQ} = \begin{pmatrix} -2 \\ 0 \end{pmatrix} \qquad \overrightarrow{XY} = \begin{pmatrix} -5 \\ 2 \end{pmatrix}$$

4 Write down the modulus (in surd form) of the vector with the longest length in question **3**.

118

1. If $k = \begin{pmatrix} 2 \\ 4 \end{pmatrix}$, $m = \begin{pmatrix} -3 \\ 2 \end{pmatrix}$ and $n = \begin{pmatrix} -5 \\ -1 \end{pmatrix}$, find as a column vector:

   a $3m$

   b $4n$

   c $m + k$

   d $2m + n$

   e $5k - n$

   f $2k + 3m + 2n$

   g $4(m - n)$

   h $\frac{1}{2}(k + 2n)$

2. Simplify the following vectors:

   a $a + 2b - b$

   b $2a + 3(a + 2b)$

   c $\frac{1}{2}(a - b) + b$

   d $a + \frac{3}{2}(b - 2a)$

   e $a + \frac{2}{3}(2a - b) + \frac{1}{2}b$

   f $3a - \frac{1}{2}(a + c) + 2b$

3. Make a copy of this grid then write on the letters A to H so that:

   a $\overrightarrow{OA} = 2a$

   b $\overrightarrow{OB} = a + 2b$

   c $\overrightarrow{OC} = -b$

   d $\overrightarrow{OD} = 2a - 2b$

   e $\overrightarrow{OE} = -2a + b$

   f $\overrightarrow{OF} = -a - b$

   g $\overrightarrow{OG} = -2a - 2b$

   h $\overrightarrow{OH} = 2a + 3b$

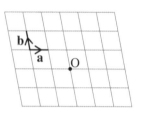

4. Express each vector in terms of a, b or c.

   a $\overrightarrow{AC}$

   b $\overrightarrow{CA}$

   c $\overrightarrow{AD}$

   d $\overrightarrow{BD}$

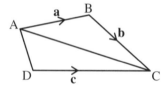

5. $\overrightarrow{KL} = \begin{pmatrix} 2 \\ 5 \end{pmatrix}$ and $\overrightarrow{MN} = \begin{pmatrix} 8 \\ 20 \end{pmatrix}$

   KL is parallel to MN. *Explain* why.

6. KLMN is a rhombus. Express each vector in terms of **m** and **n**.

   a $\overrightarrow{KN}$

   b $\overrightarrow{MN}$

   c $\overrightarrow{LN}$

   d $\overrightarrow{MK}$

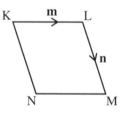

7. M has co-ordinates (3, 1)

   $\overrightarrow{MN} = \begin{pmatrix} 4 \\ 2 \end{pmatrix}$ and $\overrightarrow{MP} = \begin{pmatrix} 3 \\ -1 \end{pmatrix}$.

   a Find the co-ordinates of N.

   b Find the co-ordinates of P.

   c Find $\overrightarrow{NP}$ as a column vector.

1 $\overrightarrow{ML} = p$ and $\overrightarrow{LN} = q$.

S is the midpoint of ML and T cuts MN in the ratio $2:1$.
Express the following vectors in terms of p and q.

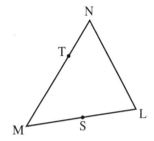

a $\overrightarrow{MS}$ **b** $\overrightarrow{MN}$ **c** $\overrightarrow{MT}$

d $\overrightarrow{ST}$ **e** $\overrightarrow{SN}$ **f** $\overrightarrow{TL}$

2 $\overrightarrow{OA} = 2\overrightarrow{OM}$; $\overrightarrow{OC} = 4\overrightarrow{ON}$

Express the following vectors in terms of a and b.

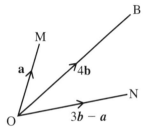

a $\overrightarrow{AB}$ **b** $\overrightarrow{AC}$

c *Explain* why A, B and C are collinear
(lie on the same straight line).

d Find the ratio $AB:AC$.

3 X cuts AB in the ratio $2:1$.

Y cuts DC in the ratio $1:2$.

Express the following vectors in terms of a and b.

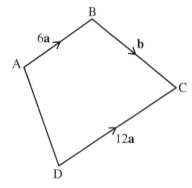

a $\overrightarrow{XY}$ **b** $\overrightarrow{AD}$

c *Explain* why AXYD is a parallelogram.

4 KLMN is a parallelogram.

P is the midpoint of MN.

$\overrightarrow{PQ} = a + 5b$

Express the following vectors in terms of a and b.

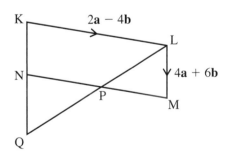

a $\overrightarrow{KN}$ **b** $\overrightarrow{LP}$ **c** $\overrightarrow{LQ}$ **d** $\overrightarrow{KQ}$

e Explain why K, N and Q are collinear
(lie on the same straight line).

f Find the ratio $KN:KQ$.

120

STATISTICS 2   11

TASK M11.1 ──────────────────────────── **Main Book Page 351**

Give answers to one decimal place when appropriate.

1 When they last recycled something, 600 children were asked if they recycled paper, bottles or cans. The information is shown in the two-way table below.

	Paper	Bottles	Cans	Total
Boys		73	89	
Girls				352
Total	306	131		600

  a Copy and complete the two-way table.

  b How many girls recycled paper last time they recycled something?

  c What percentage of the children recycled cans?

2 500 students in Years 10/11 of Kingsley High School were asked what they planned to do after Year 11. All the students will either stay in the 6th Form, go to college or do an apprenticeship.

206 students plan to stay in the 6th Form of whom 120 are in Year 11.
26 students in Year 10 want to do an apprenticeship.
31 students in Year 11 want to do an apprenticeship.
109 students in Year 11 want to go to college.

  a One of these students is picked at random. Write down the *probability* that the student is in Year 10.

  b One of these students is picked at random. Write down the *probability* that the student plans to go to college.

3 Some people were asked if they would rather watch a film on a DVD, at the cinema or go to the theatre.

The results are shown below: M = Male, F = Female
                             d = DVD, c = cinema, t = theatre

M, c	M, c	F, c	F, d	F, c
F, d	F, t	F, d	M, t	M, c
M, c	F, c	M, c	F, t	F, d
F, d	F, d	M, t	M, d	F, c

  a Put these results into a two-way table.

  b What percentage of the males chose the theatre?

4 1000 people in Birmingham and Nottingham travel to work by car, by walking, by bike or by train.

314 out of the 530 people who travel by car live in Birmingham. 69 people from Birmingham travel by train. 117 people from Birmingham walk and 175 people from Nottingham walk.

41 out of 72 people who travel by bike come from Nottingham.

a One of the people from Birmingham *only* is chosen. What is the *probability* that this person travels to work by bike?

b What percentage of the people asked travel to work by train?

TASK M11.2	Main Book Page 354

In questions **1** and **2**, work out the angle for each item and draw a pie chart.

1 Favourite type of film

Film	Frequency
adventure	6
comedy	18
horror	7
romance	2
cartoon	12

2 Favourite colour

Colour	Frequency
blue	23
green	8
red	28
yellow	41
purple	4
other	16

3 300 people were asked what their favourite hot drink is. The pie chart shows the findings.

How many people chose:

a coffee   **b** others   **c** tea

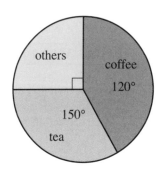

4 This pie chart shows the favourite 'spirits' chosen by 480 people.

How many people chose:

a vodka   **b** gin   **c** brandy

5 10 000 people were surveyed about which continent they would prefer to buy their car from.

The pie chart shows this information.

Find the angle on the pie chart for:

a Europe   **b** Asia   **c** America

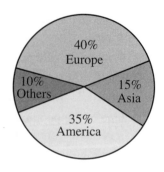

6 The pie charts show the favourite sports of students from Canning High School and Henton Park School.

Explain why you *cannot* say that more students like football in Canning High School than in Henton Park School.

TASK M11.3/M11.4   **Main Book Page 358**

1 Write down what X and Y might be to give this scatter graph.

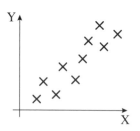

2 The table below shows the heights and neck lengths of 15 people.

Height (cm)	177	187	195	162	200	175	192	186	200	165	200	172	198	181	190
Neck length (cm)	6·9	7·5	7·5	5·5	8·5	6·1	6·8	6·8	13	6	8	5·7	7·7	6·9	7·8

a Copy and complete this scatter graph to show the data in the table on the previous page.

b Draw the line of best fit.

c One of the points does not follow the trend. Write down the values of this point.

d Describe the correlation for the points that follow the trend.

e A person is 184 cm tall. Use your line of best fit to find out the person's likely neck length.

f Another person has a neck length of 7·7 cm. How tall is that person likely to be?

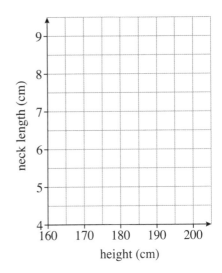

3 This scatter graph shows information about cars. Write down what you think Y might be.

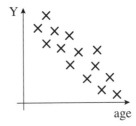

4 A golfer records his weekly average score and how many hours he practises each week (in golf a score of 70 is *better* than a score of 80!).

The information is shown in the table below.

Weekly average score	79	75	87	81	84	73	77	88	72	78	84	76
Weekly hours practising	22	24	19	21	22	23	24	17	26	22	19	21

a Draw a scatter graph to show this data. Use the *x*-axis for the weekly average score from 70 to 90. Use the *y*-axis for the weekly hours practising from 0 to 30.

b Describe the correlation in this scatter graph.

c Draw the line of best fit.

d If the golfer practised for 25 hours one week, what average score would you expect the golfer to get that week?

e An average weekly score of under 60 in golf would be impossible. Explain why the line of best fit cannot be used to work out the average score for a golfer if the golfer practises for 45 hours one week.

124

1 A local post office sells cards. The table below shows how many cards were sold during a one-year period.

Month	Jan	Feb	Mar	Apr	May	Jun	Jul	Aug	Sep	Oct	Nov	Dec
Number of cards	60	440	80	380	100	40	60	20	300	460	580	560

   a Draw a line graph for the information in this table.

   b Find the mean average for the first 4 months: Jan, Feb, Mar, Apr.
      Plot this average on the graph at the midpoint of the 4 months.

   c Keep moving along one month and finding the 4-point moving average (ie. use a group of 4 months). Plot the new moving average on the graph each time.

   d Join up the moving average points with a dotted line. Comment on the trend of card sales during this year. Write down any reasons for this trend.

2 The table below shows how many houses have been sold by an estate agent during a 15-year period.

Year	2001	2002	2003	2004	2005	2006	2007	2008	2009	2010	2011	2012	2013	2014	2015
Number of houses sold	135	45	135	150	30	180	165	60	180	135	165	195	45	180	150

   a Draw a line graph for the information in this table.

   b Find the 3-point moving average (ie. use groups of 3 years).
      Plot the new moving average on the graph each time.

   c Join up the moving average points with a dotted line. Comment on the trend of house sales during these 15 years.

3 The table below shows how many people visit a local castle each day during a 3-week period.

	Mon	Tue	Wed	Thu	Fri	Sat	Sun
Week 1	90	75	100	115	140	210	180
Week 2	55	75	114	115	147	224	187
Week 3	62	68	107	129	182	210	201

   a Draw a line graph for the information in this table.

   b Find the 7-point moving average.

   c Plot the moving average points on the graph and join them up with a dotted line.

   d Comment on the trend shown.

TASK M11.6   **Main Book Page 365**

1   Write down which samples below are likely to be representative.

For any sample which is not representative give a reason why it is not.

a   To find out the average number of cars owned by each family in a particular city.
The sample is chosen by randomly selecting 10% of the streets in the city and visiting each house to establish the number of cars.

b   To find out who people will vote for at the next Local Election in a certain town.
The sample is chosen by asking people as they enter the town's largest supermarket.

c   To find out the percentage of the crowd entering a football ground who are female.
The sample is chosen by recording the sex of every 10th person as they pass through the gates.

d   To find out the average amount of time people spend exercising each week.
The sample is chosen by asking people as they enter a local Gym.

e   To find out the average number of computers per household.
The sample is chosen by selecting at random people from 10% of the addresses from the electoral register.

f   To find out the number of birds which visit gardens in the UK.
The sample is chosen by selecting every 20th name from every telephone directory in the UK and asking each of these people to record the number of birds.

2   Describe how you would select a representative sample for each of the following:

a   To find out the most popular rock bands of people under 18 years old.

b   To find out the most popular holiday destinations of people in Scotland.

c   To survey pupils in a school about how they get to and from school each day.

d   To investigate the most popular drinks of people in a certain city.

TASK M11.7   **Main Book Page 368**

1   625 people go to the theatre to watch a famous comedian. 392 of these people are male.
A stratified sample of 50 people is to be taken from the males and females in the audience to find out their opinions on the concert. How many males and how many females will be chosen?

2   900 people return from their holidays. 284 people went skiing, 109 visited Australasia, 321 took city breaks in Europe and the rest had visited the Caribbean.
A holiday company wishes to find out about the quality of service in the hotels these people stayed in. They decide to take a stratified sample of 70 people. What should be the sample size for each of the holiday destinations: skiing, Australasia, European cities and the Caribbean?

3   Rachel needs to survey opinions from people visiting the local swimming pool.
Explain how Rachel could take a simple random sample.

4 The table below shows the number of people who voted for each party at a General Election in one constituency.

Party	Number of votes
Labour	16 201
Conservative	12 374
Liberal Democrat	9 812
Green	7 104
Others	387

It is wanted to take a stratified sample of 2000 people to find out more about their opinions on major issues.

How many people from each chosen Party would be selected in the stratified sample?

5 A 5% stratified sample of 40 people is taken from a group according to whether they can drive or not. The number of people in the sample is shown below.

	Drive	Not drive	Total
Male	18	5	23
Female	13	4	17
Total	31	9	40

What is the lowest possible number of males who do not drive in the whole group of people?

6 In a certain school, a choice from 3 languages is offered in Year 7.
The take-up is shown below.

Language	Number of pupils
French	139
German	69
Spanish	42

A sample of 25 pupils is to be taken to question them about their attitudes to languages.
a Explain why you would want to use a stratified sample.
b Work out how many pupils you would want in your sample from each Language.

ALGEBRA 3   12

TASK M12.1   Main Book Page 378

1 **a** Draw these axes.
   b If $3x + y = 6$, find the value of y when $x = 0$.
   c If $3x + y = 6$, find the value of x when $y = 0$.
   d Plot the 2 points from **b** and **c** and join them up to make the straight line $3x + y = 6$.

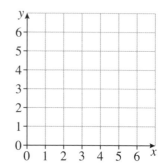

2 Draw each line below with the 'cover-up' method.
You need to find the 2 points first then draw the
axes big enough.

a $2x + 3y = 12$ **b** $3x + 7y = 21$

c $8x + 5y = 40$ **d** $4x - 3y = 24$

TASK M12.2 ———————————————————— **Main Book Page 379**

1 Use the graph to solve the simultaneous equations below:

a $x + y = 6$
     $2x - y = 6$

b $x - 2y = -6$
     $2x - y = 6$

c $x + y = 6$
     $x - 2y = -6$

2 **a** Draw an x-axis from 0 to 7.

Draw a y-axis from -5 to 5.

b Use the cover up method to draw the line $2x + 3y = 12$.

c Use the cover up method to draw the line $4x - 2y = 8$.

d Use the graph to solve the simultaneous equations $2x + 3y = 12$
                                                 $4x - 2y = 8$

3 By drawing graphs, solve the following pairs of simultaneous equations:

a $x + y = 4$
    $y = x + 2$

b $5x + 2y = 20$
    $x - 2y = -8$

c $2x + y = 7$
    $y = 2x - 5$

TASK M12.3 ———————————————————— **Main Book Page 381**

1 Add together the simultaneous equations: $3x + 2y = 7$
                                   and $7x - 2y = 3$

Use your answer to find the value of x.

Use your answer to find the value of y.

Solve the simultaneous equations

2 $2x + 3y = 12$
    $5x + 3y = 21$

3 $4x + y = 13$
    $4x + 3y = 23$

4 $3x + y = 16$
    $2x - y = 9$

5 $4x - 3y = 0$
    $7x + 3y = 33$

6 $5x + 4y = 24$
    $3x - 4y = -24$

7 $2x - 5y = -12$
    $3x - 5y = -13$

8 $4x + 2y = 10$
    $7x - 2y = 34$

9 $3x + 5y = -11$
    $3x - 4y = -2$

10 $2x - 2y = -16$
     $3x - 2y = -21$

128

Solve the simultaneous equations

1 $3x + 4y = 17$
$6x + y = 20$

2 $2a + 3b = 14$
$3a + 2b = 11$

3 $4m + 3n = 26$
$3m - 5n = -24$

4 $5c - 4d = 21$
$2c - 3d = 7$

5 $2p - 3q = -11$
$p + 4q = 11$

6 $7a + 3b = 22$
$5a - 2b = 24$

7 $3m + 4n = 11$
$2m + 6n = 9$

8 $4x - 3y = 2$
$5x + 7y = -19$

9 $10x - 3y = -14$
$4x - 5y = -17$

10 $3p - 2q + 18 = 0$
$5p + 7q = 32$

11 $8c + 3d = -35$
$5c = -22 - 2d$

12 $6x - 8y = 1$
$4x + 12y - 5 = 0$

Answer these questions by forming a pair of simultaneous equations then solving them.

1 Darren buys 3 pairs of socks and 2 pairs of underpants for £25. Colin buys 2 pairs of socks and 7 pairs of underpants for £62. What is the cost of a pair of socks and a pair of underpants.

2 The sum of two numbers is 19. The difference between four times one number and the other number is 41. Find the values of the two numbers.

3 Howlton primary school buy 10 solar calculators and 30 battery calculators for £210. Merryfield primary school buy 15 solar calculators and 8 battery calculators for £130. Find the cost of one solar calculator and one battery calculator.

4 Penny buys 5 adult tickets and 3 child tickets for the theatre. The tickets cost her a total of £164. Barney buys 4 adult tickets and 4 child tickets at a total cost of £152. Find the cost of one adult ticket and one child ticket.

5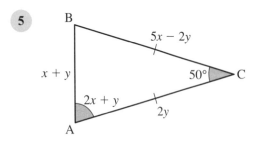

Triangle ABC is isosceles.

Work out the actual length of AB.
All lengths are in cm.

6 A straight line passes through the points $(2, 11)$ and $(-1, 2)$.
The equation of a straight line is $y = mx + c$. Find the value of m and c.

7 A bookstall is selling all its hard backs at the same price and all its paper backs at the same price. A woman buys 7 hard backs and 5 paper backs for £61·40. A man buys 11 hard backs and 7 paper backs for £93·10. Find the price of one hard back and one paper back.

8

O is the centre of the circle.

$B\hat{C}E = 2m + 3n$

$B\hat{A}C = 3m - n$

$O\hat{C}A = m$

$A\hat{C}D = 3m + 2n$

Work out the actual value of $B\hat{O}C$

9 A pub offers a special discount for senior citizens. A set meal is normally £11 but the price for a senior citizen is £8. One day the pub sells three times as many senior citizen set meals as normal priced set meals and takes £420. How many senior citizen meals and normal priced meals did the pub sell on that day?

11 Charlie has four times as many sweets as Anna. Charlie eats 14 sweets and Anna eats 2 sweets. If Charlie now has three times as many sweets as Anna, how many sweets have Charlie and Anna each got *now*?

TASK M12.6 ──────────────────────────────── **Main Book Page 385**

In question **1** to **6**, write down the next 2 numbers. What is the rule for each sequence?

1 40, 20, 10, 5, ...

2 4·9, 4·1, 3·3, 2·5, ...

3 $\frac{1}{2}, 1\frac{1}{4}, 2, 2\frac{3}{4}, ...$

4 4, 12, 36, 108, ...

5 3000, 300, 30, 3, ...

6 $-1, -2, -4, -8, ...$

7 The first four terms of a sequence are 2, 8, 14, 20. The 50th term in the sequence is 296. Write down the 49th term.

130

In questions **8** to **11** , find the next 2 numbers in each sequence (it may help you to work out the the 2nd differences).

8 2, 5, 10, 17, …   **9** 0, 3, 8, 15, …   **10** 2, 6, 12, 20, …   **11** 2, 8, 16, 26, …

12 The first five terms of a sequence are 1, 2, 4, 8, 16, …
The 9th term in the sequence is 512.
Write down the 10th term of the sequence.

13 Find the next 2 numbers in each sequence below.
  a 2, 5, 7, 12, 19, …   **b** 0, 7, 26, 63, …   **c** 1, 4, 16, 64, …   **d** 1, 1, 2, 4, 7, 13, …

14 Find the next 2 numbers in the sequence below. Try to explain the pattern.
  0, 1, 3, 7, 15, …

15 Match each nth term formula below to its corresponding sequence:
  a 1, 6, 11, 16, …
  b 2, 5, 10, 17, …
  c 5, 7, 9, 11, …
  d 2, 6, 12, 20, …
  e 3, 9, 27, 81, …
  f 4, 8, 12, 16, …

A $2n + 3$ B $n^2 + 1$

C $4n$ D 3^n

E $n(n + 1)$ F $5n - 4$

TASK M12.7   **Main Book Page 386**

1 Write down the common ratio for each geometric progression below.
  a 3, -12, 48, -192, …   **b** 4, $\frac{4}{3}, \frac{4}{9}, \frac{4}{27}$, …
  c 0·3, 0·06, 0·012, 0·0024, …   **d** 8, -4, 2., -1, …

2 The 7th term of a geometric progression is 48.
The 8th term is -16. Find the common ratio.

3 How many terms are in the geometric progression below?
     6, 18, 54, … , 4374

4 The 2nd term of a geometric progression is 28 and the 3rd term is 112.
Find the first term in the sequence.

5 The 3rd term of a geometric progression is 10 and the 5th term is 160.
Find the common ratio.

6 2, 3, 5, 8, 13, …
Write down the 10th term of the sequence above.

7 A sequence has nth term $= 3(4)^{n-1}$
Write down the first 4 terms of this sequence.

8 Write down a Fibonacci sequence.

9 Matt invests some money and receives 5% per annum compound interest. The money at the end of each year forms a geometric progression. Write down the common ratio.

10 $m, n, m + n, ...$ is a Fibonacci sequence. Write down the next four terms of this sequence.

11 Sequence A has nth term $= 2(5)^{n-1}$ and sequence B has nth term $= 4(7)^{n-1}$. Work out the difference between the 7th term of sequence A and the 4th term of sequence B.

12 A sequence has a common ratio of -3.
The 7th term of the sequence is 81. Write down the 1st term of the sequence.

TASK M12.8 ———————————————————— **Main Book Page 389**

> **Remember:**
> For an arithmetic sequence
> nth term $= a + (n - 1)d$
> where $a =$ first term and $d =$ common difference

1 Match up each arithmetic sequence to the correct nth term formula.

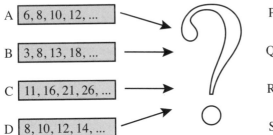

A [6, 8, 10, 12, ...]

B [3, 8, 13, 18, ...]

C [11, 16, 21, 26, ...]

D [8, 10, 12, 14, ...]

P [n^{th} term $= 2n + 6$]

Q [n^{th} term $= 5n - 2$]

R [n^{th} term $= 2n + 4$]

S [n^{th} term $= 5n + 6$]

2 Find the nth term of each arithmetic sequence below.

a 7, 10, 13, 16, ...

b 9, 16, 23, 30, ...

c 1, 10, 19, 28, ...

d 6, 14, 22, 30, ...

e 30, 26, 22, 18, ...

f 18, 13, 8, 3, ...

g 8, 12, 16, 20, ...

h 22, 19, 16, 13, ...

3 The nth term of an arithmetic sequence is $5n + 4$.

a Is 61 a term in this arithmetic sequence? Explain your answer fully.

b Find an expression for the $(n + 1)$th term

4

$n = 1$
$s = 8$

$n = 2$
$s = 15$

$n = 3$
$s =$

a Draw the next shape in the sequence.

b Let n = shape number and s = number of sticks. Complete a table of values for n and s.

c Find a formula for the number of sticks (s) for the shape number n.
Use values of n to check if the formula is correct.

d Use the formula to find out how many sticks are in shape number 40.

5 Repeat question **4** for the sequence below:

 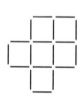 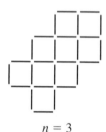

$n = 1$

$n = 2$

$n = 3$

6 Matthew decides to save money in the following way:
He saves £1 in the first week, £1·20 in the second week, £1·40 in the third week, and so on.

a How much would he save in the nth week?

b How much would he save in the 8th week?

c In which week would he save at least £5?

d After 10 weeks, Matthew wants to buy a tennis racquet which costs £19·99. He realises that he hasn't saved quite enough, but by how much is he short?

7 Which sequences below are arithmetic and which are geometric?

a 2, 6, 18, 54, ...   b 20, −10, 5, −2·5, ...   c −0·5, −1, −1·5, −2, ...

8 A series of rows of tins are piled on top of one another. The bottom row has 35 tins and each row has two fewer tins than the row below it.

a How many tins are there in the nth row from the bottom?

b What is the maximum number of rows of tins?

1 Write down the first four terms of each sequence below using the iterative formula.

    a $u_{n+1} = 12 - u_n$, $u_1 = 5$ **b** $u_{n+1} = 4u_n^2$, $u_1 = 2$

    c $u_{n+1} = \dfrac{36}{u_n}$, $u_1 = 3$ **d** $u_{n+1} = 5u_n^2 - 2u_n$, $u_1 = 1$

2 A sequence is defined by $t_{n+1} = 2t_n - t_{n-1}$ where $t_1 = 3$ and $t_2 = 4$. Find t_3, t_4 and t_5.

3 $u_{n+1} = 3 + u_n$ and $u_5 = 22$. Find a formula for u_n.

4 $y_{n+1} = 5 + y_n$ and $y_3 = 19$.

    a Find a formula for y_n.

    b Find y_{38}.

5 Write down the first four terms of each sequence below using the nth term formula.

    a $u_n = 5n^2 + 1$ **b** $u_n = 6n - 3$ **c** $u_n = 5(3)^{n-1}$

6 Sequence A is defined by $u_{n+1} = 8u_n$ and sequence B is defined by $w_{n+1} = 2w_n$ where $u_1 = w_1 = 3$.

    Write down the values of 2 terms other than 3 which are in sequence A and sequence B.

7 Write down the nth term formula for each sequence below.

    a 2, 5, 8, 11, ...   **b** 1, 2, 4, 8, ...   **c** 1·2, 1·4, 1·6, 1·8, ...

8 $u_n = 3n + 5$ for sequence A.

    $w_n = 5n - 11$ for sequence B.

    Find the term in each sequence when $u_n = w_n$.

9 $u_n = 2n^2 - 3n$. Ava works out that $u_{n+1} = 2n^2 + n + 5$

    Is she correct? Show all your working out.

10 $y_n = n^2 + 6n$. Find out the value of n algebraically when $y_{n+1} - y_n = 17$.

1 The nth term of a sequence is given by $n^2 - n$

    a Write down the 1st term of the sequence.

    b Write down the 4th term of the sequence.

    c Write down the 10th term of the sequence.

2 Find the nth term of each sequence below:

    a 5, 8, 13, 20, 29, ...   **b** −1, 2, 7, 14, 23, ...

    c 0, 2, 6, 12, 20, ...   **d** 6, 14, 24, 36, 50, ...

3 Here is a sequence of rectangles made from squares.
Let n = shape number and s = number of squares.

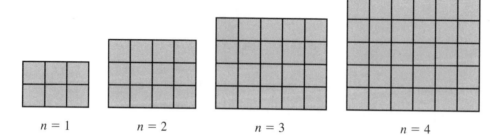

$n = 1$ $\qquad$ $n = 2$ $\qquad$ $n = 3$ $\qquad$ $n = 4$

a Find a formula for s terms of n.

b How many squares in shape number 25?

4 Find **i** the nth term and **ii** the 20th term of each sequence below:

a 3, 12, 27, 48, 75, ... $\qquad$ **b** 5, 11, 21, 35, 53, ...

c 7, 18, 33, 52, 75, ... $\qquad$ **d** 5, 18, 37, 62, 93, ...

5 Consider the sequence: $\quad -3 \quad -4 \quad -3 \quad 0 \quad 5$

a Find the nth term.

b Find the value of n for which the nth term $= 140$

TASK E12.3 $\qquad\qquad\qquad\qquad\qquad\qquad\qquad$ **Main Book Page 395**

1 A sequence is defined by $u_{n+1} = (\sqrt{5})u_n$ and $u_1 = 7$.

a Find u_2, u_3, u_4 and u_5

b Describe fully the type of sequence generated.

2 A sequence is defined by $u_n = 6(\sqrt{2})^{n-1}$.
Write down the first 5 terms of this sequence.

3 Write down the first 3 terms of the sequences given by each nth term below.

a $u_n = n(n+3)$ $\qquad$ **b** $u_n = \dfrac{n+1}{2n}$ $\qquad$ **c** $u_n = 7(\sqrt{3})^n$

4 A sequence is defined by $u_n = 2(\sqrt{3})^{n-1}$.
Write down an iterative formula for this sequence.

5 Find the formula for u_n which generates the sequence 4, $4\sqrt{7}$, 28, $28\sqrt{7}$, ...

6 Describe the sequences given by each nth term below.

a $u_n = 2n^2 + 3n$ $\qquad$ **b** $u_n = (\sqrt{6})^n$ $\qquad$ **c** $u_n = 8(\sqrt{3})^{n-1}$ $\qquad$ **d** $u_n = \dfrac{1}{5}n - 7$

7 Find the nth term of each sequence below.

a $\dfrac{2}{3^2}, \dfrac{3}{4^2}, \dfrac{4}{5^2}, \dfrac{5}{6^2}, \ldots$

b $-1, 2, 9, 20, \ldots$

c $(2 \times 3), (3 \times 4), (4 \times 5), (5 \times 6), \ldots$

d $1, 5, 25, 125, \ldots$

e $\dfrac{1 \times 3^3}{2}, \dfrac{2 \times 4^3}{3}, \dfrac{3 \times 5^3}{4}, \dfrac{4 \times 6^3}{5}, \ldots$

f $5, 5\sqrt{6}, 30, 30\sqrt{6}, \ldots$

8 A sequence is defined by $u_{n+1} = \pi u_n$ and $u_1 = \sqrt{2}$.

a Find u_9 and u_{10}

b Write down the formula for the nth term of this sequence.

c Describe this sequence fully.

TASK E12.4 ——————————————————— **Main Book Page 398**

1 $(x + 3)^2 = (x + 3)(x + 3) = x^2 + 6x + 9$

Express $x^2 + 6x + 13$ in the form $(x + a)^2 + b$, giving the values of a and b.

2 $(x - 5)^2 = (x - 5)(x - 5) = x^2 - 10x + 25$

Express $x^2 - 10x + 18$ in the form $(x + c)^2 + d$, giving the values of c and d.

3 Write the following in the form $(x + a)^2 + b$ where a and b are numbers to be determined:

a $x^2 + 16x + 30$ **b** $x^2 - 4x + 1$ **c** $x^2 - 3x + 2$

4 Copy and complete:
$$x^2 - 8x + 3 = 0$$
$$(x - 4)^2 - \square + 3 = 0$$
$$(x - 4)^2 = \square$$
$$x - 4 = \sqrt{\square} \ \text{ or } -\sqrt{\square}$$
$$x = 4 + \sqrt{\square} \ \text{ or } 4 - \sqrt{\square}$$

5 Solve the following quadratic equations by completing the square (leaving your answers in the form $a \pm \sqrt{b}$ where appropriate):

a $x^2 + 6x + 4 = 0$ **b** $x^2 - 12x + 21 = 0$

c $x^2 - 20x + 90 = 0$ **d** $x^2 + 5x + 2 = 0$

6 $3x^2 + 18x + 42 = a((x + b)^2 + c)$. Find the values of a, b and c.

7 $4x^2 - 16x + 44 = p((x - q)^2 + r)$. Find the values of p, q and r.

8 $5x^2 + 30x - 7 = a(x + b)^2 + c$. Find the values of a, b and c.

9 $2x^2 + 5x + 1 = p(x + q)^2 + r$. Find the values of p, q and r.

10 Solve $2x^2 + 16x + 26 = 0$ by completing the square, giving your answer to 3 significant figures.

136

1 Write down the co-ordinates of the turning point of each function below.

    a $y = (x + 4)^2 + 3$ **b** $y = (6 - x)^2 - 2$

    c $y = (3x - 1)^2 + 4$ **d** $y = (5 + 4x)^2 - 1$

2 Find the co-ordinates of the turning point of $y = x^2 + 10x + 19$ by completing the square.

3 Find the co-ordinates of the minimum point of $y = x^2 - 8x + 13$.

4 Find the equation of the line of symmetry of the curve shown opposite.

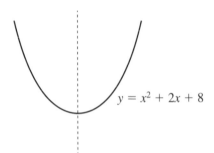

$y = x^2 + 2x + 8$

5 Find the minimum y-value of the curve $y = x^2 - 4x + 7$.

6 Find the equation of the line of symmetry of the curve $y = 4\left(x - \dfrac{1}{2}\right)^2 + 3$.

7 Find the minimum value of $2x^2 - x + 1$.
    (This means the minimum y-value of $y = 2x^2 - x + 1$)

8 Find the equation of the curve shown opposite, giving the answer in the form $y = x^2 + ax + b$.

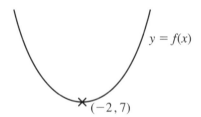

$y = f(x)$

$(-2, 7)$

9 **a** Explain clearly why $y = 3x^2 + 24x + 53$ is always positive (hint: complete the square).

    b Describe where $y = 3x^2 + 24x + 53$ would be positioned on a graph.

10 By completing the square on the denominator, find the maximum value of the function

    $f(x) = \dfrac{6}{x^2 + 6x + 11}$. What value of x gives this maximum value?

> **LEARN!**
> if $ax^2 + bx + c = 0$ then $x = \dfrac{-b \pm \sqrt{b^2 - 4ac}}{2a}$

Use the formula to solve the following quadratic equations, giving each answer to 3 significant figures.

1 $x^2 + 9x + 4 = 0$ **2** $x^2 + 4x - 1 = 0$ **3** $x^2 - 6x - 2 = 0$

4 $x^2 + 8x + 3 = 0$ **5** $2x^2 + 3x - 7 = 0$ **6** $5x^2 + 9x + 1 = 0$

7 $2x(2x - 3) = 1$ **8** $9x^2 + 5x - 2 = 0$ **9** $3x + \dfrac{3}{x} = 7$

Use the formula to solve the following quadratic equations, leaving each answer in the form $\dfrac{p \pm \sqrt{q}}{r}$.

10 $x^2 + 5x + 3 = 0$ **11** $5x^2 - 2x - 4 = 0$ **12** $x + 7 + \dfrac{11}{x} = 0$

In this Exercise give answers to 3 significant figures when appropriate.

1 A rectangle is such that its length is 2 metres longer than its width.
   a If the width of a rectangle is x metres then find expressions for the length and the area of the rectangle in terms of x.
   b If the area is 5 m², show that $x^2 + 2x - 5 = 0$.
   c Solve this equation to find the value of x.

2 A rectangle is 34 m longer than it is wide. If the diagonal of the rectangle is 50 m then:
   a By letting the width be x, prove that $x^2 + 34x - 672 = 0$.
   b Solve this equation to find the dimensions of the rectangle.

3 A triangle whose area is 76 cm² is such that the base is 3 cm longer than twice the height. If the height of the triangle is h then:
   a Write down an expression for the base of the triangle in terms of h.
   b Write down a quadratic equation involving h.
   c Solve this equation to find h (you may use the fact that $19 \times 16 = 304$).

4 50 m of fencing is arranged so that it encloses a rectangular area of 154 m². If w is the width of the rectangle then:
   a Find the length of the rectangle in terms of w.
   b Write down a quadratic equation involving w.
   c Solve this equation to find w.

5 Two positive numbers are such that the bigger one is 3 less than twice the smaller one. Their product is 35. If the smaller of the two numbers is x then:

   a Write down an expression for the larger number in terms of x.

   b Write down a quadratic equation involving x.

   c Solve this equation to find x.

6 Two circles are cut out of a rectangular sheet of metal. The larger circle has a radius r and the smaller circle has a radius 5 cm less than the larger circle. If the shaded area is $250\,cm^2$, find the radius of the smaller circle.

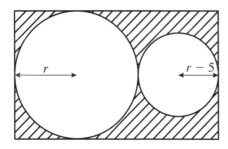

TASK E12.8 ———————————————— **Main Book Page 404**

Solve the following simultaneous equations.

1 $y = x^2 + 4$
   $y = 3x + 2$

2 $x^2 - y^2 = 20$
   $x - y = 2$

3 $x^2 - 6y = 15$
   $2x + y = 5$

4 $xy = 12$
   $y = 2x - 2$

5 **a** Find the co-ordinates of M and N by solving the simultaneous equations
     $y = 7 - 3x$
     $y = 5 - x^2$

   b Work out the 'exact' length MN.

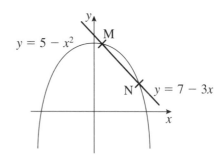

6 The line $y = 2x - 1$ meets the curve $\dfrac{x^2}{9} + \dfrac{y^2}{4} = 1$ at two points.

Find the co-ordinates of each point, giving the answers to 2 decimal places.

TASK E12.9 ———————————————————— **Main Book Page 406**

> **Remember:**
> $x^2 + y^2 = r^2$ is the equation of a circle of radius r with its centre at $(0, 0)$.

1 Write down the 'exact' radius of each circle below.

    a $x^2 + y^2 = 64$ **b** $x^2 + y^2 = 18$ **c** $x^2 + y^2 = 50$

2 Write down the equation of each circle with centre at the origin $(0, 0)$ and the following:

    a radius $= 9$ **b** radius $= 3\sqrt{5}$ **c** diameter $= 8\sqrt{2}$

3 Find the points of intersection of the circle $x^2 + y^2 = 20$ and the line $y = 5x - 6$.

4 Calculate the length AB.

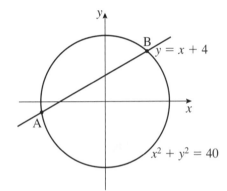

5

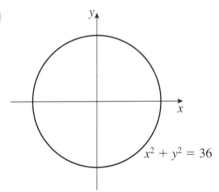

Prove that the point $(2, 5)$ lies inside the circle $x^2 + y^2 = 36$.

6 Line PQ passes through $(0, 1)$ and is perpendicular to the line $x + y = 3$.
Find the co-ordinates of the points where the line PQ intersects the circle $x^2 + y^2 = 25$.

140

1 Find the equation of the tangent to the circle $x^2 + y^2 = 18$ at $(3, 3)$.

2 Find the equation of the tangent to the circle $x^2 + y^2 = 20$ at $(-4, -2)$.

3 Find the equation of the tangent to the circle $x^2 + y^2 = 32$ at (m, n).

4

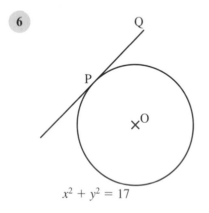

O is the origin $(0, 0)$, and the centre of the circle.
A has co-ordinates $(-5, 2)$.
Find the equation of the tangent at B.

5 The point $(6, 3)$ lies on a circle with centre at $(2, 1)$.
Find the equation of the radius which joins $(2, 1)$ to $(6, 3)$.

6

Q

P

$\times^O$

$x^2 + y^2 = 17$

The point Q lies on the tangent to the circle $x^2 + y^2 = 17$ at $P(-4, 1)$.
The x-value at Q is -1.
Work out the 'exact' length OQ.

7 The equation of a tangent to a point A on a circle is $5x + 3y = 34$.
The centre of the circle is $(0, 0)$. Find the co-ordinates of point A.

8 One circle has its centre at (10, 5). Line l_1 is the tangent to this circle at (12, 1). Line l_2 is the tangent to the circle $x^2 + y^2 = 13$ at (2, 3). Lines l_1 and l_2 meet at P. Find the co-ordinates of P.

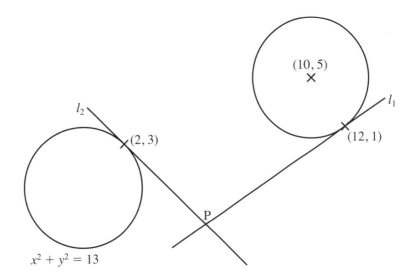

TASK E12.11 — **Main Book Page 409**

1 **a** Using a table of values, plot the graph of $y = 3^x$ from -3 to 3.

b Use your graph to find the value of $3^{1\cdot8}$

c Use your graph to solve $3^x = 13$

d Find the gradient of the tangent at $x = 1\cdot5$

2 The population in the town of Carwick is in decline. The population, P, after t years is given by the formula

$$P = 2000\,(0\cdot97)^t$$

a Find the initial population P.

b Find the population after 5 years.

c Plot a graph showing the population over the first 10 years.

d After how many years will the population have declined to 1600 (give your answer to 1 decimal place)?

e Estimate the rate at which the population is decreasing after 6 years.

3 The curve $y = pq^x$ passes through (0, 4) and (2, 36).

a Find the value of p.

b Find the value of q (q is a positive constant).

c Find the value of y when $x = 3$.

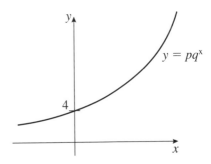

4 The curve $y = 5n^{-x} + c$ passes through $(0, 2)$ and $\left(1, -\frac{1}{2}\right)$.

   a Find the value of c.

   b Find the value of n.

   c Find the value of y when $x = 2$.

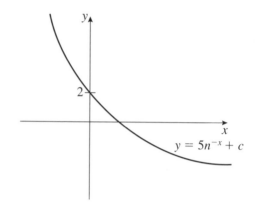

5 £500 is invested in a bank at 4% per annum compound interest.
Let A be the amount of money in the account after t years.

   a Write down a formula $A = m(n)^t$ where m and n are numbers to be found.

   b Find the value of A (to the nearest penny) after 14 years.

TASK M12.9   **Main Book Page 413**

1 Use this graph to find the roots (to one decimal place) of:

   a $x^2 + 5x + 1 = 0$

   b $x^2 + 5x + 1 = 2x + 4$

   c $x^2 + 3x - 3 = 0$

   d $x^2 + 5x + 2 = 0$

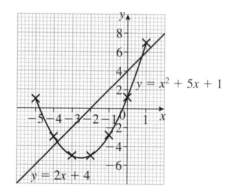

2 Use this graph to find the roots (to one decimal place) of:

   a $x^2 - 3x - 2 = 0$

   b $x^2 - 3x - 3 = 0$

   c $x^2 - 3x + 1 = 0$

   d $x^2 - 3x - 2 = 2 - 2x$

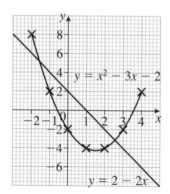

3 **a** Draw the graph of $y = x^2 - 2x$ for x-values from -2 to 4.

  b On the same axes, draw the graph of $y = x + 1$.

  c Use your graphs to find the roots (to one decimal place) of:

   i $x^2 - 2x = 1$ **ii** $x^2 - 2x - 4 = 0$ **iii** $x^2 - 2x = x + 1$ **iv** $x^2 - 3x - 1 = 0$

4 If the graph of $y = x^2 + 4x - 2$ has been drawn, write down the equation of each line which should be drawn to solve each of the following equations:

  a $x^2 + 4x - 2 = 3x + 1$ **b** $x^2 + 3x - 2 = 0$ **c** $x^2 + 5x - 4 = 0$

GEOMETRY 4   13

| TASK M13.1 | **Main Book Page 424** |

Give answers to one decimal place if necessary.

Find the area of each shape below. All lengths are in cm.

1

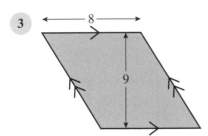

2

3

4 The area of the parallelogram is equal to the area of the trapezium.
Find the value of x.

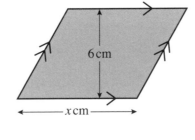

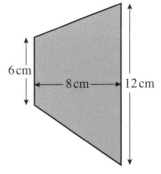

5 Find the shaded area.

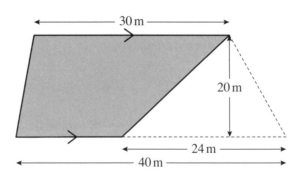

6 Find the shaded area.

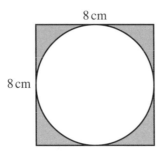

7 Find the area of each shape. All arcs are either semi-circles or quarter circles and the units are cm.

a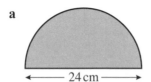

b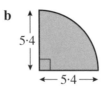

c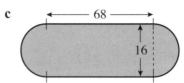

8 Find each shaded area below. All lengths are in cm.

a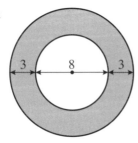

b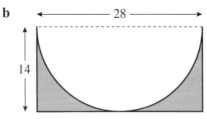

c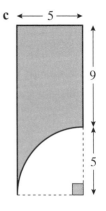

9 A circular pond has a radius of 13 m. A path goes all the way round the circumference of the pond. The path is 1·2 m wide throughout.

Find the area of the path.

10 Calculate the radius of a circle of area 68 cm².

11 The area of this parallelogram is $112 \cdot 5 \text{ cm}^2$.
Calculate the value of x.

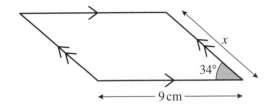

12 Find the area of this regular pentagon.

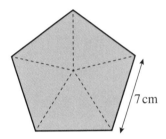

7 cm

| **TASK E13.1** | **Main Book Page 427** |

Find the area of each triangle below, giving the answer to one decimal place.

1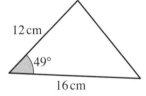
12 cm
49°
16 cm

2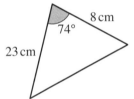
8 cm
74°
23 cm

3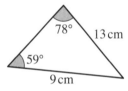
78°
13 cm
59°
9 cm

Find the value of the letter in each triangle below.

4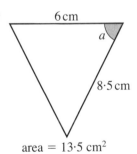
6 cm
a
8·5 cm
area = 13·5 cm²

5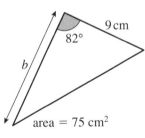
9 cm
82°
b
area = 75 cm²

6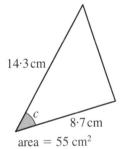
14·3 cm
c
8·7 cm
area = 55 cm²

7 Area triangle ABC = 48 cm²
Area triangle ABD = 120 cm²
Calculate the length of CD.

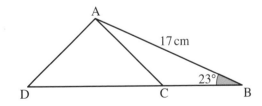
A
17 cm
23°
D   C   B

8

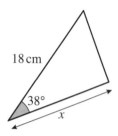

The area of this triangle is equal to the area of this trapezium. Calculate the value of x.

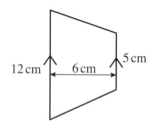

9 Calculate the area of the pentagon ABCDE if BC = CD.

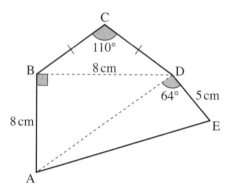

TASK M13.2 ──────────────────────────── **Main Book Page 429**

In this Exercise, O is always the centre of the circle. Give answers to one decimal place.

1 Find the length of arc AB.

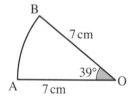

2 Find the length of arc AB.

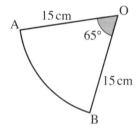

3 The arc PQ = 9 cm.
Find $P\hat{O}Q$.

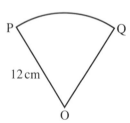

In questions ④ to ⑥, find the perimeter of each shape, leaving answers in terms of π.

4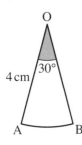

5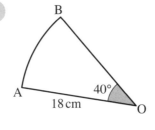

6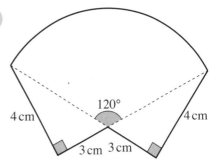

7 Use a calculator to find the perimeter of the shaded area.

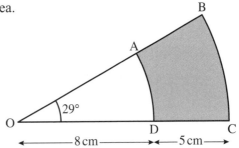

8 Use a calculator to find the perimeter of the shaded area.

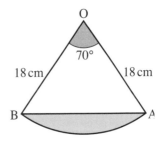

9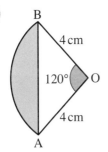

Prove that the 'exact' perimeter of the shaded region is $\left(\dfrac{8\pi}{3} + 4\sqrt{3}\right)$ cm.

In this Exercise, O is always the centre of the circle. Give answers to one decimal place.

In questions **1** to **3**, find each shaded area.

1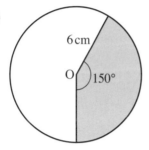

2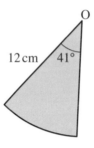

3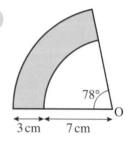

4 Show that the area of this sector is exactly $\dfrac{16\pi}{9}$ cm².

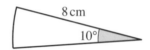

5 ODC is a sector of radius 4 cm.
Find the shaded area, leaving your
answer in terms of π.

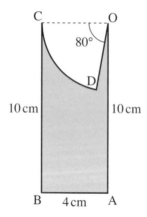

6 Find the value of θ if the area of
the sector is 90 cm².

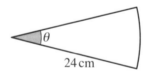

7 Find the area of the shaded segment.

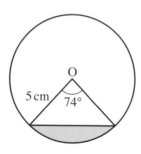

8 If AB = 13 cm, find the area of the shaded segment.

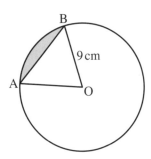

9 cm

9

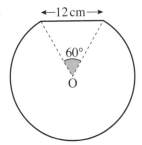

Prove that the 'exact' area of the
major segment opposite is $12(10\pi + 3\sqrt{3})\,cm^2$.

10

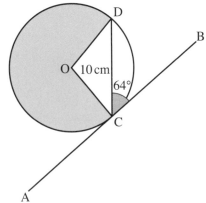

AB is a tangent to the circle. CD = 10 cm.
Calculate the area of the shaded major sector.

TASK M13.5/13.6 ———————————————————— **Main Book Page 437**

Remember: $1\,m^3 = 1000\,\ell = 1\,000\,000\,cm^3$
$1\,m^2 = 10\,000\,cm^2$

1 Find the volume of each prism below:

a

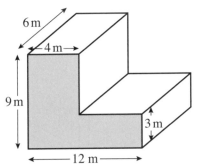

b

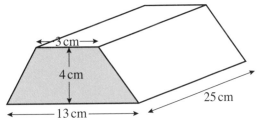

2 Which is the greater amount? $7\cdot2\,\text{m}^3$ or $7\,090\,000\,\text{cm}^3$

3 True or false? $6\cdot3\,\text{m}^2 = 630\,\text{cm}^2$

4 A rectangular tank has a length of 8 m and a width of 6 m.
How high is the tank if it can hold $240\,000$ litres of water when full?

5 Copy and complete

a $4\,\text{m}^3 = \boxed{}\,\text{cm}^3$ **b** $2\cdot9\,\text{m}^3 = \boxed{}\,\text{cm}^3$ **c** $8\,\text{m}^2 = \boxed{}\,\text{cm}^2$

d $7\cdot48\,\text{m}^2 = \boxed{}\,\text{cm}^2$ **e** $6\,000\,000\,\text{cm}^3 = \boxed{}\,\text{m}^3$ **f** $6\,\text{m}^3 = \boxed{}\,\text{litres}$

g $6\,000\,000\,\text{cm}^2 = \boxed{}\,\text{m}^2$ **h** $5\cdot16\,\text{m}^3 = \boxed{}\,\text{litres}$ **i** $38\,000\,\text{cm}^2 = \boxed{}\,\text{m}^2$

6 Find the 'exact' volume of each prism below, leaving your answers in terms of π.

a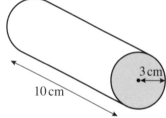

b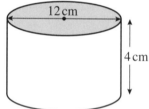

7 A pipe of diameter 8 cm and length 3 m is
half full of water. How many litres of
water are in the pipe?

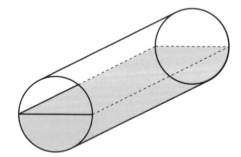

8 The cylinder opposite is made with
metal of density $9\,\text{g/cm}^3$.

Prove that the mass of the prism
is 'exactly' 3024π grams.

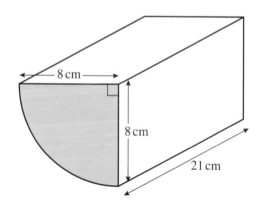

9 A cylindrical bucket has a diameter of 30 cm and a height of 35 cm.

How many full bucket loads of water are needed to fill up the tank opposite?

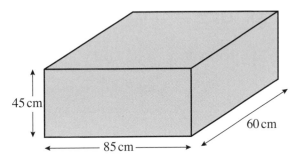

10 The height of a cylinder of capacity 3·5 litres is twice its radius.

Calculate the radius of the cylinder.

11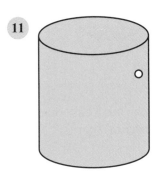

A barrel has a 25 cm diameter.

The barrel is empty then water is poured in at a rate of 0·05 litres per second.

There is a hole in the barrel. The water enters the barrel for 5 minutes 14 seconds before it starts leaking through the hole.

Calculate the height of the hole above the base of the barrel.

12 A small piece of chocolate is in the shape of a prism.

Its length is 10 cm and its cross-sectional area is the segment of a circle with centre at O as shown.

The density of the chocolate is 0·95 mg/mm³.

Calculate the mass of this piece of chocolate.

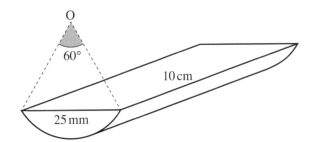

TASK M13.7 ———————————————————————————— **Main Book Page 441**

> **Remember:** sphere   pyramid   cone
>
> volume $= \frac{4}{3}\pi r^3$ volume $= \frac{1}{3} \times$ (base area) $\times h$ volume $= \frac{1}{3}\pi r^2 h$

In this Exercise give answers to 3 significant figures where necessary.

1 Find the volume of each solid.

a

14 cm

←—— 23 cm ——→

b

4 m

3 m

←—— 7 m ——→

c

2·5 m

2 A hemisphere and a cone are both made from the same material. The cone has a base diameter of 8 cm and a perpendicular height of 6 cm. The hemisphere has a diameter of 7 cm. Which solid weighs more?

3 A sphere has a volume of 80 cm³. Find the radius of the sphere.

4 Find the 'exact' volume of each solid, leaving your answers in terms of π.

a

4 cm

3 cm

16 cm

15 cm

b

9 cm

25 cm

(hemisphere on a cylinder)

5 A bowl is in the shape of a hemisphere with diameter of 18 cm. Water is poured into the bowl at a rate of 12 cm³/s. How long will it take to fill the bowl completely?

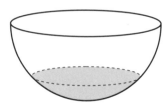

6 A pyramid has a square base of side length 8 cm and a perpendicular height of 17 cm. The pyramid has the same volume as a cone of base radius 6·5 cm. Find the perpendicular height of the cone.

7 A metal cylinder has diameter 4·8 cm and a height of 8·3 cm. 75 identical cylinders are melted down to make a single sphere. Calculate the diameter of the sphere.

TASK M13.8 ──────────────────────────── **Main Book Page 445**

> **Remember:**   sphere   cylinder   cone
>
> surface area = $4\pi r^2$ curved surface area = $2\pi rh$ curved surface area = πrl
> where l is the slant height

In this Exercise give answers to 3 significant figures where necessary.

1 Find the *curved* surface area of each solid.

a 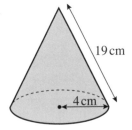   **b** 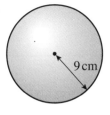   **c**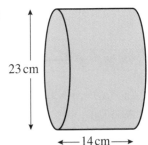

2 Find the *total* surface area of this cone, leaving your answer in terms of π.

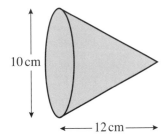

3 A sphere has a surface area of 480 cm². Calculate its diameter.

4 The curved surface area of a hemisphere is 72π cm². What is the 'exact' *total* surface area of the hemisphere?

5 A cone is attached to a cylinder of diameter 15 cm as shown. The perpendicular heights of the cylinder and the cone are both equal to the diameter of the cylinder. Find the *total* surface area of the combined solid.

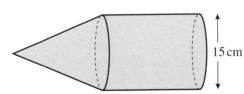

6 The total surface area of a cylinder is $112\pi\,\text{cm}^2$.

    a Show that $r^2 + 10r - 56 = 0$ if r is the radius and the length of the cylinder is $10\,\text{cm}$.

    b Work out the radius of this cylinder.

7

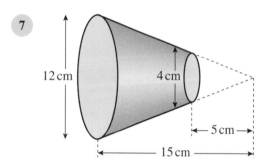

Calculate the total surface area of the frustum opposite.

8 A cylinder has a radius of $2\,\text{cm}$ and a height of $10\,\text{cm}$. A cone has a radius of $3\,\text{cm}$. The total surface area of the cone is equal to the total surface area of the cylinder. Show that the perpendicular height of the cone is $4\sqrt{10}\,\text{cm}$.

TASK M13.9 ──────────────────────────────── **Main Book Page 448**

1   **a** *Explain* why these triangles are similar.

     b Find x.

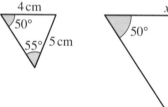
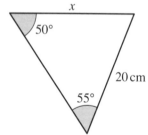

2 Rectangles A and B are similar.

    Find x.

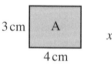
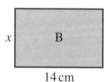

3 Shapes C and D are similar.

    Find y and z.

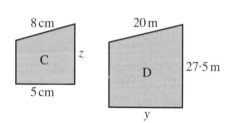

4 Use similar triangles to find x.

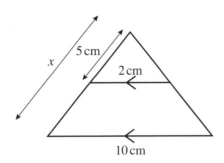

5 **a** Prove that triangles ABE and ACD are similar.

b Find the value of y.

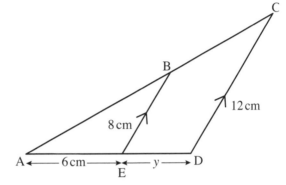

6 Use similar triangles to find x in each diagram below.

a

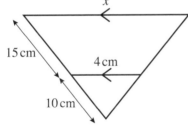

b

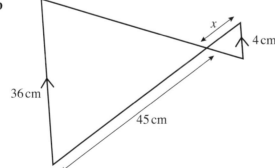

TASK M13.10 ——————————————————————— **Main Book Page 450**

In questions **1** to **3** , find x.

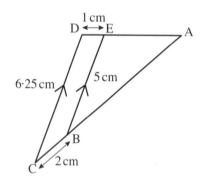

1
3 cm
5 cm
1·5 cm
x

2
3 cm
8 cm
6 cm
x

3
9 cm
7 cm
14 cm
x

4 Find AB and AE.

1 cm
D ← → E
A
6·25 cm
5 cm
B
C
2 cm

5 QP̂R = SR̂T.

PQ = 3 cm, RT = 5 cm and PR = 4·2 cm.

Work out the length RS.
Justify your answer fully.

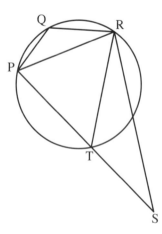

Q R
P
T
S

6 **a** *Explain* why triangles PQR and STR are similar.

 b Find the length of ST.

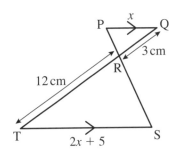

7 Find x and y.

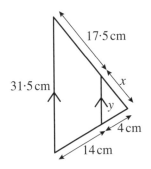

8 Find x.

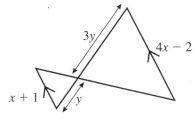

9 Find x and y.

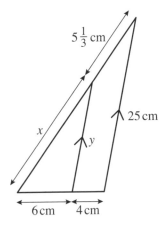

| **TASK E13.1** | **Main Book Page 454** |

1 Find the volume of the larger of these 2 similar cylinders.

volume $= 32\,\text{cm}^3$

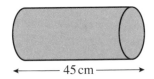

2 These prisms are similar. The total surface area of the smaller prism is $19\,\text{cm}^2$.

Find the total surface area of the larger prism.

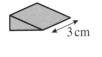

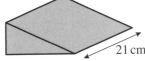

158

3 These cones are similar.
Find h.

21 cm

h

surface area
= 576 cm²

surface area
= 16 cm²

4 A factory makes two footballs and they charge a fixed price *per square metre* of leather that is used to cover the football. If they charge £12 for the football of radius 15 cm, how much do they charge for a football of radius 12 cm?

5 Two triangles are similar. The area of the larger triangle is 6 m² and its base is 5 m. How long (to the nearest cm) is the base of the smaller triangle if its area is 1 m²?

6 The cost of similar bottles of milk is proportional to the *volume*. A bottle which has a radius of 36 mm costs 75p.
  a What is the price (to the nearest pence) of the bottle with a radius of 45 mm?
  b What is the radius (to 3 sig. figs.) of the bottle which costs £1?

7 These two containers are similar. The ratio of their diameters is 3 : 7. Find the capacity of the smaller container if the larger container has a capacity of 34 litres (give your answer to 3 sig. figs.).

8 A shop sells bars of soap in various sizes, all of which are similar to each other. The shop charges the same amount per cm³ of soap in each bar. If the bar which is 5 cm long costs 80p then what is the price (to the nearest pence) of the bar which is 8 cm long?

| **TASK E13.2** | **Main Book Page 457** |

1 These two shapes are similar.
If the volume of A is 47 cm³, find:
  a the area ratio
  b the length ratio
  c the volume ratio
  d the volume of B

A

surface area
= 13 cm²

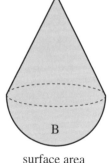

B

surface area
= 468 cm²

2 These two hemispheres are similar.
If the surface area of Q is 912 cm³, find:

    a the volume ratio

    b the length ratio

    c the area ratio

    d the surface area of P

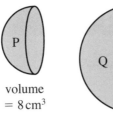

volume = 8 cm³

volume = 512 cm³

3 Two hexagonal prisms are similar. One has a capacity of 5·4 *l* and the other has a capacity of 6·9 *l*. If the surface area of the smaller one is 19 m², what is the surface area (to 3 sig. figs.) of the larger one?

4 A bottle has a surface area of 480 cm² and a volume of 700 cm³. What is the surface area (to 3 sig. figs.) of a bottle whose volume is 500 cm³?

5 A towel has a volume of 6100 cm³. The towel shrinks in a tumble drier. It remains a similar shape but its surface area is reduced by 12%. Find the new volume of the towel (to 3 sig. figs.).

6 Two crystals are similar. Their surface areas are in the ratio 5 : 9. If the volume of the smaller crystal is 8·7 mm³, find the volume of the larger crystal (to 3 sig. figs.).

7 Two cones are similar.
Their volumes are shown opposite.
Calculate the radius of the smaller cone if the height of the larger cone is 12 cm.

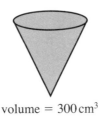

volume = 300 cm³

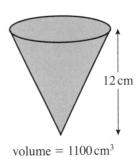

12 cm

volume = 1100 cm³

8 Two similar solid statues are made from the same material. The surface area of the larger statue is 2749 cm² and the smaller statue is 1364 cm². The cost of the material to make the larger statue is £490. What is the cost of the material to make the smaller statue (to the nearest pence)?

STATISTICS 3   14

TASK M14.1   Main Book Page 468

You may use a calculator for this Exercise.

1 For each set of numbers below, find

    i the mean   **ii** the median   **iii** the mode   **iv** the range

    a 6   10   9   3   16   10   2

    b 8   11   4   8   15   4   16   5   10

2 The ages of the members of a football team are:

       19   27   22   21   24   33   29   26   22   18   31

    Two players are 'sent off' in a match. They are the 29 year-old and the 18 year-old. Find the mean age of the players left on the pitch.

3 Seven people score the following marks in a test:

       30   40   40   40   45   45   96

    Find

    a the mean

    b the median

    c which average best describes these marks? *Explain why.*

4 In a shooting match, Rose scores:

       8   9   9   9   10   9   9   9   9   10

    Find

    a the mode

    b the mean

    c Which average best describes these scores, the mode or the mean? *Explain why.*

5

    ☐   4   ☐   9   ☐

    Ross has 5 cards. The 5 cards have a mean of 7, a median of 7 and a range of 13. What are the 5 numbers on the cards?

6 The mean average age of 6 people is 37. What is the total of all their ages?

7 The mean weight of 11 people is 63 kg.

    a What is the total weight of all 11 people?

    b One person of weight 83 kg leaves the group. Find the mean weight of the remaining 10 people.

8 The mean average salary of 7 people is £26 500. Gemma joins the group. If she earns £32 100, what is the mean average salary of all 8 people.

9 The mean amount of weekly pocket money for 36 boys is £4·50. The mean amount of weekly pocket money for 14 girls is £5·50. Find the mean amount of weekly pocket money for all 50 children.

10 100 people are surveyed about their weekly pay. 50 people from Banford have mean average pay of £460. 30 people in Darrington have mean average pay of £340. 20 people from Dalton have mean average pay equal to the mean average pay of all 100 people. Find the mean average pay of all 100 people.

11 $(n - 2), (n - 1), n, (n + 1), (n + 2)$ are five consecutive integers. Find and simplify an expression for the mean average of the squares of these five integers.

TASK M14.2 — **Main Book Page 471**

1 The table below shows the number of drinks some children had during one day.

Number of drinks	1	2	3	4	5
Frequency	7	12	8	23	29

Find **a** the modal number of drinks

b the median number of drinks

2 The 2 tables below show the number of GCSE grade 5's obtained by some students.

Number of grade 5's	1	2	3	4	5
Frequency	20	38	18	27	24

Boys

Number of grade 5's	1	2	3	4	5
Frequency	26	20	41	39	67

Girls

a Find the median number of grade 5's for the boys.

b Find the median number of grade 5's for the girls.

c Which group has the higher median number of grade 5's?

3 The table below shows how many times some people ate meat during one week.

Number of times meat eaten	0 to 1	2 to 5	6 to 8	over 8
Frequency	75	n	104	17

Find **a** the modal interval if $n = 51$

b the interval which contains the median if $n = 195$

c the largest value of n if the interval containing the median is '6 to 8'.

4 Some students from nearby schools are asked how often they go each month to a local skateboard park. The information is shown in the tables below.

Chetley Park School	
Park Visits	**Frequency**
0 to 1	27
2 to 5	21
6 to 9	15
10 or more	8

Wetton School	
Park Visits	**Frequency**
0 to 1	19
2 to 5	23
6 to 9	34
10 or more	17

a For each school, find the interval which contains the median.

b From which school do students generally go to the skateboard park more often? Explain why you think this.

TASK M14.3 ──────────────────────────────── **Main Book Page 472**

Use a calculator if you need to.

1 Some young people were asked how many different mobile phones they had owned during the last 6 years. The information is shown in the table below.

Number of phones	0	1	2	3	4
Frequency	7	4	12	14	3

a Find the total number of phones.

b Find the mean average number of phones.

2 Some people were asked how many computers they had in total in their houses.

a Find the total number of computers.

b Find the mean average number of computers per house (give your answer to 1 decimal place).

Number of computers	Frequency
0	16
1	26
2	37
3	20
4	5

3 Some teenagers in 2 areas of a city were asked how many pairs of shoes they owned.
The results are shown in the tables below.

Area A

Number of pairs of shoes	1	2	3	4	5	6
Frequency	5	11	28	24	8	3

Area B

Number of pairs of shoes	1	2	3	4	5	6
Frequency	1	6	23	61	42	24

a Work out the mean number of pairs of shoes for each area, giving your answers to one decimal place.

b In which area do your results suggest that teenagers own more pairs of shoes per person?

4 Some people were asked how many portions of vegetables they ate last Sunday. The amounts are shown in the table below.

Number of portions	0	1	2	3	4	5	6
Frequency	5	14	n	23	n	9	5

An equal number of people said they had 2 portions as had 4 portions.
The mean average number of portions was 2·875.
How many people said they had 2 portions of vegetables?

TASK M14.4   **Main Book Page 475**

Use a calculator if you need to.

1 Some people were asked how many times they ate out in a restaurant or pub during one month. The information is shown below.

Number of meals (m)	$0 \leqslant m < 2$	$2 \leqslant m < 5$	$5 \leqslant m < 10$	$10 \leqslant m < 20$
Frequency	24	39	16	12

  a Estimate the total number of meals (beware: number of meals are discrete values).

  b Estimate the mean average (give your answer to the nearest whole number).

  c *Explain* why your answer is an estimate.

2 The number of goals scored by two hockey teams over the last 15 years is shown in the tables below.

Batton City	
Number of goals (g)	Frequency
$20 \leqslant g < 30$	2
$30 \leqslant g < 40$	3
$40 \leqslant g < 50$	5
$50 \leqslant g < 60$	4
$60 \leqslant g < 70$	1

Chorley Town	
Number of goals (g)	Frequency
$20 \leqslant g < 30$	2
$30 \leqslant g < 40$	6
$40 \leqslant g < 50$	4
$50 \leqslant g < 60$	3
$60 \leqslant g < 70$	0

  a Which team has scored the higher mean average number of goals?

  b Write down the value of the higher mean average (give your answer to one decimal place).

  c What is the *difference* between the mean average number of goals scored by each team?

3 The weights of rugby players in 2 squads are shown in the tables below.

Weight w (kg)	$75 \leqslant w < 85$	$85 \leqslant w < 95$	$95 \leqslant w < 100$	$100 \leqslant w < 110$	$110 \leqslant w < 120$
Frequency	2	2	3	5	3

Callum hornets

Weight w (kg)	$75 \leqslant w < 85$	$85 \leqslant w < 95$	$95 \leqslant w < 100$	$100 \leqslant w < 110$	$110 \leqslant w < 120$
Frequency	1	5	2	n	1

Eastham sharks

The mean average weight for the Callum hornets is $2\frac{1}{6}$ kg more than the mean average weight for the Eastham sharks.
Use these averages to work out the value of n.
Show all your working out clearly.

TASK E14.1 ——————————————————————— **Main Book Page 477**

For each set of data below, work out the:

a median   **b** lower quartile   **c** upper quartile   **d** interquartile range

1 3   6   6   7   9   9   9   10   11   12   14   14   16   17   17

2 0·8   0·9   0·4   0·8   0·5   0·4   0·9   1·3   1·2   0·6   0·9

3 $\frac{1}{3}$ $\frac{7}{8}$ $\frac{1}{2}$ $\frac{1}{10}$ $\frac{1}{4}$ $\frac{3}{4}$ $\frac{2}{3}$

4 The cost of the last seven garments of clothing bought by Carl are (in pounds):
   32   7   12   65   28   13   23
   The cost of the last eleven garments of clothing bought by Bron are (in pounds):
   24   6   14   13   29   19   4   81   12   25   17
   a Find the median cost for each person.
   b Find the interquartile range for each person.
   c Use the medians and the interquartile ranges to compare the costs of the garments of clothing bought by Carl and Bron.

1 Two hundred 17–19 year-olds are asked how many hours of driving practice they have had.

Hours of driving (h)	Frequency
$0 \leqslant h < 10$	12
$10 \leqslant h < 20$	31
$20 \leqslant h < 30$	59
$30 \leqslant h < 40$	45
$40 \leqslant h < 50$	27
$50 \leqslant h < 60$	18
$60 \leqslant h < 70$	8

a Copy the table, adding a cumulative frequency column.

b Draw a cumulative frequency graph.

c Use the graph to estimate

  i the median and

  ii the interquartile range.

d What percentage of these people have had 43 or more hours of driving?

2 This cumulative frequency graph shows the weights of 70 children of different ages who play at a local football club.
Use the graph to estimate:

a the median weight

b the lower quartile

c the upper quartile

d the interquartile range

e how many children weighed 78 kg or more?

f What percentage of the children were within 5 kg of the median weight?

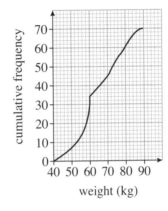

3 Some 18 year-olds planning to go to University are asked if they have saved any money towards it and, if so, how much. The information is shown in the table below:

Money saved m (£)	Frequency
$0 \leqslant m < 500$	34
$500 \leqslant m < 1000$	27
$1000 \leqslant m < 1500$	45
$1500 \leqslant m < 2000$	31
$2000 \leqslant m < 2500$	15
$2500 \leqslant m < 3000$	8
$3000 \leqslant m < 3500$	7
$3500 \leqslant m < 4000$	5

a Copy the table, adding a cumulative frequency column.

b Draw a cumulative frequency graph.

c Use the graph to estimate

  i the median and

  ii the interquartile range.

d What percentage of these 18 year-olds have saved more than £2400?

166

483

TASK E14.3 ———————————————————————— **Main Book Page 483**

1 Some people were asked about the age of their
fathers when they were born.
The information is shown in the box plot opposite:

Find **a** the median   **b** the range

      c the lower quartile   **d** the upper quartile

      e the interquartile range

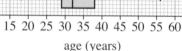

15 20 25 30 35 40 45 50 55 60
age (years)

2 Some people were asked how many
days they had been absent from work
for illness in the last year.
The results are shown in the
table opposite.
Draw a box plot to show this data.

	Days off for illness
lowest value	0
highest value	23
median	7
lower quartile	5
upper quartile	12

3 The box plots opposite show the best times for a group
of boys and girls when running the 100 m sprint.

Use the medians, ranges and interquartile ranges
to compare the times for the boys and girls.

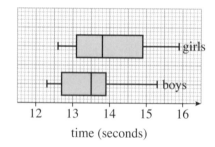

12   13   14   15   16
time (seconds)

4 Two groups of men and women were asked how long they spent on average taking a bath.
A summary of the findings is shown below.

	Time spent by men (minutes)	Time spent by women (minutes)
lowest value	3	5
highest value	55	56
median	18	19
lower quartile	11	10
upper quartile	25	25

a Draw a box plot for each group of people.

b Compare the time spent in the bath by these groups of men and women.

5 This cumulative frequency graph shows the average time per night spent on homework by pupils in class 11X.

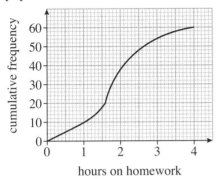

hours on homework

The box plot below shows the average time per night spent on homework by pupils in class 11Y.

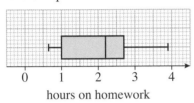

hours on homework

Comment on the differences in the time spent on homework by pupils in the two classes.

TASK E14.4 ──────────────────────────── **Main Book Page 486**

1 A number of schoolchildren were asked how long they took from getting out of bed to leaving for school on an average morning. The information is shown in the table opposite.

a Work out the frequency density for each class interval.

b Draw a histogram to illustrate this data.

Time t (minutes)	Frequency
$10 \leqslant t < 15$	25
$15 \leqslant t < 25$	70
$25 \leqslant t < 30$	60
$30 \leqslant t < 40$	80
$40 \leqslant t < 60$	100
$60 \leqslant t < 90$	60

2 The table below shows the ages at which a number of people living in a village took out pension plans.

Age (years)	20–24	25–34	35–39	40–44	45–59	60–69
Frequency	22	32	28	49	99	37

a Explain why the '25–34' class when written as an inequality is $25 \leqslant A < 35$ where A is the age.

b Explain why the frequency density for the '25–34' class is 3·2.

c Draw a histogram to illustrate this data.

3 The heights of a number of students in a school are recorded (to the nearest cm). The information is shown below.

Height (cm)	140–149	150–153	154–159	160–163	164–171	172–181	182–199
Frequency	33	6	27	26	68	57	36

a Explain why the '154–159' class when written as an inequality is $153·5 \leqslant h < 159·5$ where h is the height.

b Explain why the frequency density for the '154–159' class is 4·5.

c Draw a histogram.

TASK E14.5 ──────────────────────────── **Main Book Page 489**

1 This histogram shows the number of hours of exercise taken by a group of people each week.

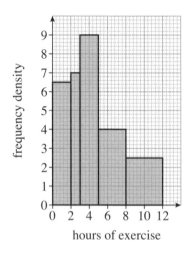

a Copy and complete the frequency table below.

Hours of exercise (h)	Frequency
$0 \leqslant h < 2$	
$2 \leqslant h < 3$	
$3 \leqslant h < 5$	
$5 \leqslant h < 8$	
$8 \leqslant h < 12$	

b What is the total frequency?

2 This histogram shows the ages of some members of a drama group.
Copy and complete the frequency table below.

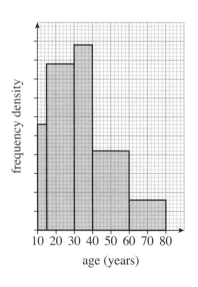

Age A (years)	Frequency
$10 \leqslant A < 15$	
$15 \leqslant A < 30$	
$30 \leqslant A < 40$	
$40 \leqslant A < 60$	42
$60 \leqslant A < 80$	

3 This histogram shows the percentage of rubbish which is recycled by households in the village of Grensham.

a Copy and complete the frequency table below.

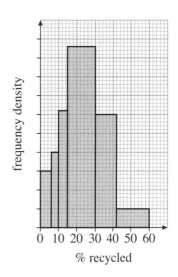

frequency density

% recycled

% recycled R	Frequency
$0 \leqslant R < 6$	
$6 \leqslant R < 10$	
$10 \leqslant R < 15$	31
$15 \leqslant R < 30$	
$30 \leqslant R < 42$	
$42 \leqslant R < 60$	

b What is the total frequency?

c What percentage of the houses recycle between 34% and 42% of their rubbish (give your answer to 1 decimal place)?

4 The unfinished histogram and table below show the annual salaries of the employees of a particular company.

Salary s (£1000s)	Frequency
$5 \leqslant s < 15$	175
$15 \leqslant s < 20$	
$20 \leqslant s < 25$	105
$25 \leqslant s < 40$	285
$40 \leqslant s < 70$	

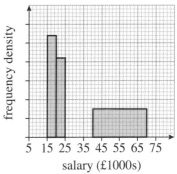

frequency density

salary (£1000s)

a Use the information shown on the histogram to copy and complete the table.

b Use the information shown in the table to copy and complete the histogram.

c What percentage of the employees earn more than £60 000? (Give your answer to 1 decimal place.)

d Estimate the mean salary (correct to the nearest £).

1 The table below shows the number of e-mails received by children in class 10P during January.

Number of e-mails	0–10	11–20	21–30	31–40	41–50	51–60
Frequency	7	4	9	6	6	2

The box plot below shows the number of e-mails received by children in class 10Q during January.

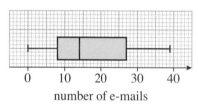

number of e-mails

a Draw a cumulative frequency graph for the number of e-mails received by children in class 10P.

b Find the median and interquartile range from this cumulative frequency graph.
Use these to compare the distribution of the number of e-mails for class 10P and 10Q.

2 The heights of the players in two hockey teams, the Tampton Trojans and Mallow Town, are shown in the back-to-back stem and leaf diagram.

Compare the heights of the players in each hockey team.

The Tampton Trojans		Mallow Town
	15	6
9 3	16	1 8 8
8 5 5 2 1	17	2 4 7 7
4 4 3	18	3
6	19	0 2

Key 2|17 = 172   Key 18|3 = 183

3 Some 8 year-olds and some 18 year-olds are asked how many Christmas presents they had last Christmas.

a Estimate the mean average for the 8 year-olds.

b Compare the number of Christmas presents received by the 8 year-olds and the 18 year-olds.

8 year-olds	
0 to 8	6
9 to 16	31
17 to 24	48
25 to 32	10
33 to 40	3
41 to 48	2

18 year-olds	
0 to 8	34
9 to 16	26
17 to 24	9
25 to 32	5
33 to 40	1
41 to 48	0

4 The histogram below shows the ages in country A at which a sample of women gave birth to their first child.

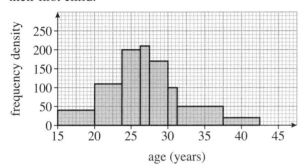

age (years)

The table below shows the ages in country B at which a sample of women gave birth to their first child.

Age A (years)	$15 \leqslant A < 18$	$18 \leqslant A < 20$	$20 \leqslant A < 21$	$21 \leqslant A < 23$	$23 \leqslant A < 28$	$28 \leqslant A < 35$
Frequency	240	320	240	460	500	140

a Using the same scale as the above histogram, draw a histogram to illustrate the data for country B.

b Compare the distribution of the ages at which women gave birth to their first child in countries A and B.

ALGEBRA 4 16

TASK M16.1 ———————————————————————— **Main Book Page 509**

Write down the inequalities shown below:

1 **a**
6

b 2 —— 6

c −2 —— 3

2 Write down all the integer values (whole numbers) of x which satisfy each inequality below.

a $4 \leqslant x \leqslant 7$ **b** $0 < x \leqslant 5$ **c** $-4 \leqslant x < -1$ **d** $-6 < x < 1$

3 Solve the inequalities below:

a $3x + 2 > 17$ **b** $2(x + 3) < 18$ **c** $6x - 4 > 3x + 17$

d $\frac{x}{2} > -5$ **e** $6(x - 2) \geqslant 24$ **f** $\frac{x}{4} - 3 \leqslant 3$

4 Find the range of values of x which satisfy each inequality below and show each answer on a number line.

a $3 + x < 6$ **b** $2 \leqslant x - 1 \leqslant 4$ **c** $-2 \leqslant 3x + 4 < 7$

5 In each case below find all the integer values of x which satisfy both the inequalities.

  a $x + 3 \leqslant 7$ and $x - 1 > 1$ 　　　　　　　 **b** $4x - 3 \geqslant 5$ and $7x + 2 \leqslant 37$

6 Write down the greatest positive integer n which satisfies each inequality below:

  a $4 - 9n > -23$ 　　　 **b** $\dfrac{4n + 3}{7} \leqslant 5$ 　　　 **c** $-1 - 5n \geqslant -8$

7 Solve each inequality below and show each answer on a number line.

  a $2 - 3x > 4 - x$ 　　　 **b** $5(x - 2) \geqslant 3(3x + 2)$ 　　　 **c** $1 \leqslant \dfrac{2x - 3}{5} \leqslant 5$

TASK E16.1 　　　　　　　　　　　　　　　　 **Main Book Page 511**

1 Display each set below on a number line.

  a $\{x : x \geqslant -2\}$ 　　　　　　　　 **b** $\{x : -4 < x < 2\}$

  c $\{x : -1 \leqslant x < 5\}$ 　　　　　　 **d** $\{x : x < -2 \text{ or } x > 1\}$

2 Use set notation to describe each number line.

3 The perimeter of this rectangle is less than or equal to 54 cm. Use set notation to describe the possible set of values for x.

$5x + 3$

$3x$

4 Write in set notation the solutions for the inequalities below.

  a $7 < x + 2 < 17$ 　　　　　　　　 **b** $-3 \leqslant \dfrac{x}{4} \leqslant 2$

  c $20 \leqslant 5x \leqslant 45$ 　　　　　　　 **d** $11 \leqslant 6x - 1 < 29$

  e $-5 < \dfrac{3x + 1}{4} < 4$ 　　　　　 **f** $-24 < 2(5x + 3) \leqslant 16$

  g $x + 2 \leqslant 5x - 1 \leqslant x + 3$ 　　　 **h** $2 - 3x < 2(4x + 1) < 5 - 3x$

5 Use set notation to write down the possible values of x for which $y > 0$ for the curve shown opposite.

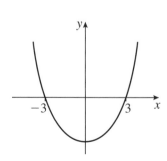

1 Write down the inequality which describes the shaded region.

a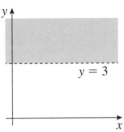

$y = 3$

b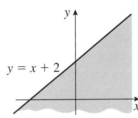

$y = x + 2$

c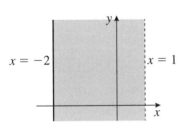

$x = -2$ $x = 1$

d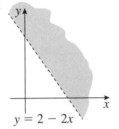

$y = 2 - 2x$

2 For each shaded region, write down the 3 inequalities which describe it.

a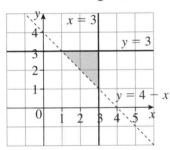

$x = 3$, $y = 3$, $y = 4 - x$

b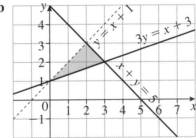

$y = x + 1$, $3y = x + 3$, $y = 5$

3 Draw graphs to show the regions given by the inequalities below:

a $2 \leqslant y \leqslant 5$ **b** $y < x + 3$ **c** $3x + 4y \geqslant 12$

4 Draw a graph to show the region defined by all 3 inequalities given below.
Shade the required region.

$y \geqslant x - 1$ $5x + 6y \leqslant 30$ $x > 1$

5 By finding the equation of each boundary line, write down
the 3 inequalities which describe this shaded region.

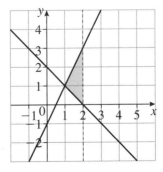

6　**a** Draw x and y-axes from -3 to 5.

　b If x and y are integers only, mark with a $\times$ all co-ordinates which lie in the region defined by the 3 inequalities below.

$$y > x - 2 \qquad\qquad x > -2 \qquad\qquad x + y \leqslant 3$$

　(You should end up plotting 16 crosses)

7　Some people attend a small theatre show. Adults pay £6 each and students pay £5 each. During one show a maximum of £150 is taken from ticket sales. There are at least twice as many adults as students at the show. Some students definitely attend the show.

Let x be the number of students and y be the number of adults.

Use inequalities to work out the maximum number of people who might have attended this show.

TASK E16.3 ———————————————————————————— **Main Book Page 515**

1　Sketch $y = (x - 2)(x + 4)$ then solve $(x - 2)(x + 4) < 0$

2　**a** Factorise $x^2 - 4x + 3$

　b Sketch $y = x^2 - 4x + 3$

　c Solve $x^2 - 4x + 3 \geqslant 0$

3　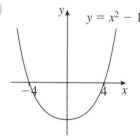 Use the graph opposite to solve $x^2 - 16 > 0$

$y = x^2 - 16$

4　Solve $2x^2 < 2$ and show the answer on a number line.

5　Solve the inequalities below:

　a $3z^2 - 5 < 7$ 　　　　　　**b** $x^2 - 5x - 14 \geqslant 0$ 　　　　　**c** $x^2 - 6x + 5 < 0$

　d $y^2 + 4y \leqslant 12$ 　　　　　**e** $m^2 > 6m - 8$ 　　　　　　**f** $7(x^2 - 3) \leqslant 42$

6　Solve $2(3y^2 - 1) \geqslant 88 - 4y^2$ and show the answer on a number line.

7　Solve $(x - 3)^2 \leqslant 4$ and show the answer on a number line.

8　Solve $6x^2 + 11x - 10 > 0$

9 **a** Solve the equation $x^2 - 2x - 2 = 0$ giving the answers in the 'exact' form $a \pm \sqrt{b}$.

b Give 'exact' solutions to the inequality $x^2 - 2x \leqslant 2$

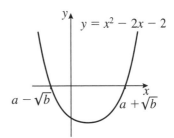

TASK E16.4 ──────────────────────────── **Main Book Page 517**

1 Write down whether each statement is true or false.

a $\dfrac{3mn - n^2}{mn} = \dfrac{3m - n}{m}$

b $\dfrac{x^2 + y^2}{xy} = x + y$

c $\dfrac{a^2 - 9}{3a^2} = -3$

d $\dfrac{4x^2}{x + 2} = 2x$

e $\dfrac{a^2 + 3a}{ab} = \dfrac{a + 3}{b}$

f $\dfrac{4m^2 - n^2}{2m} = 2m - n^2$

2 Simplify

a $\dfrac{6a}{12b}$

b $\dfrac{x^2}{xy}$

c $\dfrac{9mn}{12m^2}$

d $\dfrac{a + b}{ab}$

e $\dfrac{12x - 8y}{4}$

f $\dfrac{ab + ac}{ad}$

g $\dfrac{3x + 7y}{6x + 14y}$

h $\dfrac{4m^2}{8m - 20mn}$

3 Simplify these fractions by cancelling as far as possible.

a $\dfrac{2x^2 - 6x}{2x}$

b $\dfrac{10ab + 5b^2}{6a + 3b}$

c $\dfrac{12mn - 8m^2}{3mn - 2m^2}$

d $\dfrac{3a^2 - 9ab}{a^2 + 3ab}$

e $\dfrac{x^2 + 4x + 3}{x^2 + 3x}$

f $\dfrac{x^2 + 2x - 8}{2x^2 - 4x}$

g $\dfrac{n^2 - 6n}{n^2 - 3n - 18}$

h $\dfrac{a^2 + 3a - 4}{a^2 - 16}$

i $\dfrac{n^2 + 8n + 15}{n^2 + 3n - 10}$

j $\dfrac{a^2 - 9}{a(a + 3)}$

k $\dfrac{2w^2 + 3w + 1}{4w^2 - 1}$

l $\dfrac{6x^2 - x - 2}{3x^2 + 7x - 6}$

TASK E16.5 ──────────────────────────── **Main Book Page 519**

Simplify

1 $\dfrac{4a}{b} \times \dfrac{b}{a}$

2 $\dfrac{x}{y} \times \dfrac{y}{x}$

3 $\dfrac{6a^2}{3b} \times \dfrac{3b}{9a}$

4 $\dfrac{3x - 2}{4} \times \dfrac{8x + 3}{9x - 6}$

5 $\dfrac{5m}{4n} \div \dfrac{3}{2n}$

6 $\dfrac{2x - 1}{4y} \div \dfrac{6x - 3}{y^2}$

7 Show that $\dfrac{x + 3}{x^2 - 9} \times \dfrac{x^2 - x - 6}{x^2 + 3x + 2}$ is equivalent to $\dfrac{4x - 12}{x^2 - 3x - 4} \div \dfrac{4x^2 - 12x}{x^2 - 4x}$

176

Simplify as far as possible.

8 $\dfrac{x^2 + 4x + 3}{5x + 15} \times \dfrac{x^2 - 4x}{x^2 - 3x - 4}$

9 $\dfrac{a^2 + 5a + 6}{a^2 + 3a} \times \dfrac{a^2 + 5a - 6}{a^2 + a - 2}$

10 $\dfrac{n^2 - 5n}{n^2 - n - 2} \times \dfrac{n^2 - 4}{n^2 - 3n - 10}$

11 $\dfrac{3a^2}{a^2 - 1} \times \dfrac{a^2 + 6a - 7}{a^2 + 7a}$

12 $\dfrac{m^2 - 3m}{m^2 + 4m} \div \dfrac{m^2 + 5m}{m^2 + 9m + 20}$

13 $\dfrac{x^2 - x - 12}{x^2 - 6x + 8} \div \dfrac{x^2 + 4x + 3}{x^2 + 3x - 10}$

14 $\dfrac{b^2 + 6b - 16}{b^2 - 6b + 8} \div \dfrac{b^2 + 11b + 24}{b^2 - 8b + 16}$

15 $\dfrac{n^2 - 12n + 32}{3n^2 - 24n} \times \dfrac{7n^2 + 28n}{n^2 - 16}$

16 $\dfrac{3x^2 - 11x - 4}{5x^2 - 16x + 3} \div \dfrac{6x^2 + 11x + 3}{10x^2 + 13x - 3}$

TASK E16.6   **Main Book Page 520**

Simplify

1 $\dfrac{a}{4} + \dfrac{a}{3}$

2 $\dfrac{3m}{4} - \dfrac{2n}{3}$

3 $\dfrac{x}{y} + \dfrac{2y}{x}$

4 $\dfrac{4}{5m} + \dfrac{2}{3n}$

5 $\dfrac{2}{3a} - \dfrac{1}{7b}$

6 $\dfrac{n + 3}{2} + \dfrac{n + 4}{5}$

7 $\dfrac{a + 6}{3} - \dfrac{a}{4}$

8 $\dfrac{5x}{8} + \dfrac{x - 3}{6}$

Write as a single fraction:

9 $\dfrac{5}{x + 2} + \dfrac{3}{x + 4}$

10 $\dfrac{7}{n + 5} + \dfrac{2}{n + 3}$

11 $\dfrac{4}{y + 6} - \dfrac{3}{y + 5}$

12 $\dfrac{8}{m + 1} - \dfrac{3}{m - 4}$

13 $\dfrac{4}{2a + 3} - \dfrac{1}{4a - 1}$

14 $\dfrac{9}{a - b} + \dfrac{4}{b - a}$

Simplify

15 $\dfrac{3}{(x + 2)(x + 3)} + \dfrac{4}{x + 2}$

16 $\dfrac{6}{n + 5} + \dfrac{2}{n^2 + 3n - 10}$

17 $\dfrac{3}{w - 1} - \dfrac{15}{w^2 + 3w - 4}$

18 $\dfrac{8}{m - 4} + \dfrac{3}{m^2 - 16}$

19 $\dfrac{2}{y^2 - 9} + \dfrac{1}{y^2 + 9y + 18}$

20 $\dfrac{5}{x^2 + 7x + 12} + \dfrac{4}{x^2 + 5x + 4}$

21 $\dfrac{5}{n - 3} + \dfrac{7}{n^2 - 9} - \dfrac{4}{n + 5}$

22 $\dfrac{3}{4 + \sqrt{x}} + \dfrac{3}{4 - \sqrt{x}}$

23 Josh adds two algebraic fractions as shown below:

$$\frac{3}{(x+2)(x-4)} + \frac{2}{x+4} = \frac{3}{(x+2)(x-4)} + \frac{\overset{1}{\cancel{2}}}{x+\cancel{4}_2}$$

$$= \frac{3}{(x+2)(x-4)} + \frac{1}{x+2}$$

$$= \frac{3}{(x+2)(x-4)} + \frac{x-4}{(x+2)(x-4)}$$

$$= \frac{x-1}{(x+2)(x-4)}$$

Is Josh correct? If not, explain any mistakes he made.

TASK E16.7 ——————————————————————— **Main Book Page 522**

1 Solve

  a $\dfrac{x+4}{7} + \dfrac{x}{3} = 2$ **b** $m - \dfrac{15}{m} = 14$ **c** $\dfrac{n-5}{3} + \dfrac{n+2}{2} = 16$

2 Show that $\dfrac{2}{x-1} + \dfrac{1}{x+4} = 2$ is equivalent to $2x^2 + 3x - 15 = 0$

3 Show that $\dfrac{2}{x+5} + \dfrac{3}{x+1} = 6$ is equivalent to $6x^2 + 31x + 13 = 0$

4 Solve these equations. Give the answers to 3 significant figures when necessary.

  a $\dfrac{3}{x} + \dfrac{2}{x+3} = 1$ **b** $\dfrac{3}{m+1} + \dfrac{8}{m+2} = 3$

  c $\dfrac{6}{w+3} + \dfrac{5}{w-2} = 9$ **d** $\dfrac{4}{x-3} - \dfrac{1}{x+1} = 2$

5 A motorbike travels 50 m at a speed v which is greater than 15 m/s. It then travels 200 m at a speed of 5 m/s less than its speed for the first 50 m. The motorbike takes 12 seconds to complete the 250 m.

  a Write down an equation involving its speed v and show that it simplifies to $6v^2 - 155v + 125 = 0$.

  b Solve this equation to find v.

6 The perimeter of this rectangle is 4 cm.

Write down an equation involving x and solve it to find x.

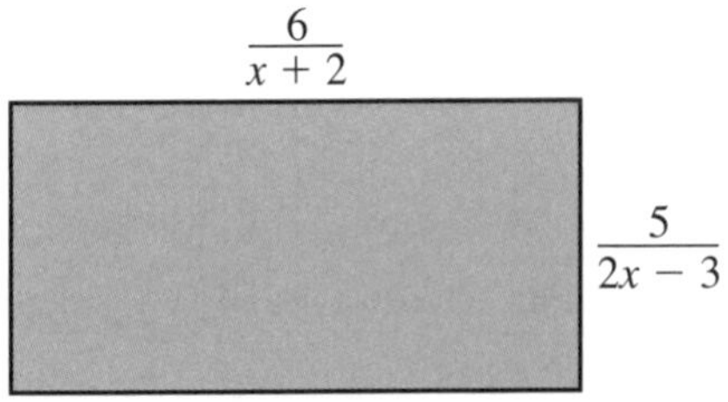

7

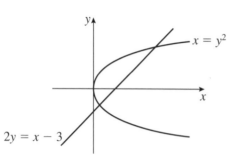

Work out the co-ordinates of the points of intersection of the line $2y = x - 3$ and the curve $x = y^2$.

TASK E16.8 ——————————————— **Main Book Page 525**

1 Use algebra to prove that the sum of 2 odd numbers is even.

2 Prove that $(n + 2)^2 - (n + 1)^2 = 2n + 3$.

3 Prove that $(n + 1)^2 + (n + 3)^2 - 10 = 2n(n + 4)$.

4 Prove that $A\hat{O}C = 2 \times A\hat{B}C$, ie. the angle at the centre of a circle is twice the angle at the circumference.

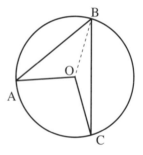

5 Prove that the difference between the squares of 2 consecutive odd numbers is a multiple of 8.

6 Prove that the sum of the squares of consecutive integers is odd.

7 A sequence is formed as follows:

$$1 \times 4 = 4$$
$$2 \times 5 = 10$$
$$3 \times 6 = 18$$
$$4 \times 7 = 28$$
$$\vdots \qquad \vdots$$

a Write down a formula for the nth term.

b Explain why the formula for the $(n + 1)$th term is $(n + 1)(n + 4)$.

c Prove that the difference between two consecutive terms in the sequence is $2n + 4$.

8   The curved surface area of a cone is twice its base area.
    Prove that the perpendicular height of the cone is $r\sqrt{3}$ cm
    where r is the radius of the cone in cm.

    (reminder: curved surface area of a cone is $\pi r l$
    where l is the slant height)

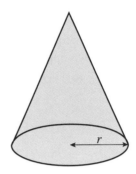

9   Prove that the sum of the squares of three consecutive odd numbers less 35 is a multiple of 12.

10 $n^2 + n$ is always an even number if n is a positive integer. Prove that the difference between the
    cubes of consecutive positive integers is always 1 more than a multiple of 6.

GEOMETRY 5   17

TASK M17.1 ──────────────────────────────── **Main Book Page 534**

1   The model of a statue is made using a scale of $1 : 40$. If the statue is $3 \cdot 2$ m tall, how tall is the
    model (give your answer in cm)?

2   A park is 5 cm long on a map whose scale is $1 : 40\,000$. Find the actual length (in km) of
    the park.

3   Copy and complete the table below.

Map length	Scale	Real length
7 cm	$1 : 60$	m
5 cm	$1 : 2000$	m
8 cm	$1 : 50\,000$	km
cm	$1 : 100\,000$	3 km
cm	$1 : 4000$	320 m
cm	$1 : 5\,000\,000$	125 km

4   The distance between two towns is 25 km. How far apart will they be on a map of scale
    $1 : 500\,000$?

5   A plan of a house is made using a scale of $1 : 30$. The width of the house on the plan is 40 cm.
    What is the real width of the house (give your answer in metres)?

6 A map has a scale of 1 : 60 000.

    a What is the actual area (in km²) of the shape ABCD shown opposite?

    b What is the real size of AB̂C?

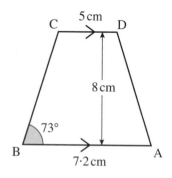

7 A park has an area of 4·5 cm² on a map with a scale of 1 : 100 000. What is the actual area of the park in hectares (1 hectare = 10 000 m²)?

8 A lake has an area of 2·25 hectares. What is the area of the lake on a map if the scale of the map is 1 : 4000?

TASK M17.2	Main Book Page 536

1 Draw AB̂C = 70°.
Construct the bisector of the angle.
Use a protractor to check that each half of the angle now measures 35°.

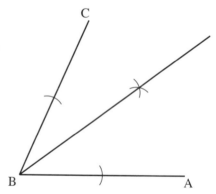

2 Draw any angle and construct the bisector of this angle.

3 Draw a horizontal line AB of length 7 cm.
Construct the perpendicular bisector of AB.
Check that each half of the line measures 3·5 cm exactly.

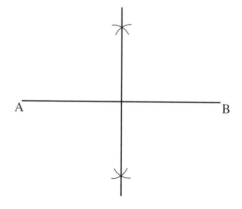

4 Draw any vertical line. Construct the perpendicular bisector of the line.

5 Construct accurately the diagrams below:

a Measure angle x and side y.

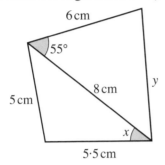

b Measure angle x and angle y.

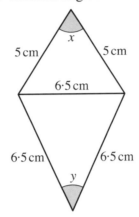

6 **a** Draw PQ and QR at right angles to each other as shown.
  b Construct the perpendicular bisector of QR.
  c Construct the perpendicular bisector of PQ.
  d The two perpendicular bisectors meet at a point (label this as S). Measure QS.

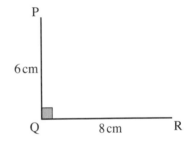

TASK M17.3 ———————————————— **Main Book Page 538**

1 Construct an equilateral triangle with each side equal to 7 cm.

2 Construct an angle of 60°.

3 **a** Draw a line 8 cm long and mark the point A as shown.

  b Construct an angle of 90° at A.

4 **a** Draw a line 10 cm long and mark the point B on the line as shown.

  b Construct an angle of 45° at B.

182

5 Construct a right-angled triangle ABC, where $A\hat{B}C = 90°$, BC = 6 cm and $A\hat{C}B = 60°$. Measure the length of AB.

6 Construct this triangle with ruler and compasses only. Measure x.

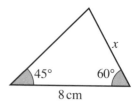

7 Draw any line and any point A. Construct the perpendicular from the point A to the line.

• A

8

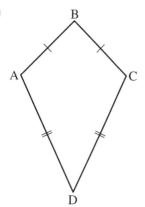

Construct the kite shown opposite with AC = 6 cm, AB = BC = 5 cm and the whole kite area = 33 cm². Measure the length AD.

| **TASK M17.4** | **Main Book Page 542** |

You will need a ruler and a pair of compasses.

1 Draw the locus of all points which are less than or equal to 3 cm from a point A.

2 Draw the locus of all points which are exactly 4 cm from a point B.

3 Draw the locus of all points which are exactly 4 cm from the line PQ.

P   5 cm   Q

4 A triangular garden has a tree at the corner B.
The whole garden is made into a lawn except for anywhere
less than or equal to 6 m from the tree. Using a scale of
1 cm for 3 m, draw the garden and shade in the lawn.

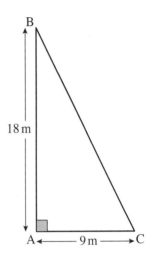

5 In a field a goat is attached by a rope to a peg P as shown.
The rope is 30 m long. Using a scale of 1 cm for 10 m,
copy the diagram then shade the area that the goat
can roam in.

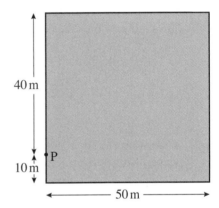

6 Draw the square opposite.
Draw the locus of all the points *outside* the square
which are 3 cm from edge of the square.

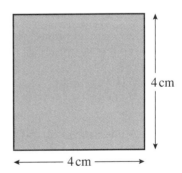

7 Each square is 1 m wide. The shaded
area shows a building.
A guard dog is attached by a chain
5 m long to the point A on the outside
of the building.
Draw the diagram on squared paper
then shade the region the dog can cover.

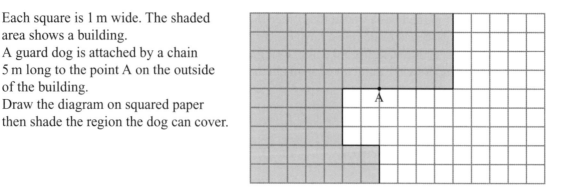

TASK M17.5 ———————————————— **Main Book Page 543**

You will need a ruler and a pair of compasses.

1 Construct the locus of points which are the same distance from the
lines AB and BC (the bisector of angle B).

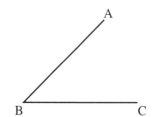

2 Faye wants to lay a path in her garden that is always the
same distance from KL and KN.
Using a scale of 1 cm for 10 m, draw the garden and construct
a line to show where the path will be laid.

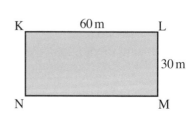

3 Construct the locus of points which are
equidistant (the same distance) from M and N.

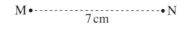

4 Draw A and B 7 cm apart.

A •   • B

A radar at A has a range of 150 km and a radar at B has a range of 90 km. Using a scale of 1 cm
for every 30 km, show the area which can be covered by both radars at the same time.

5 Draw one copy of this diagram.

a Construct the perpendicular bisector of FG and the bisector
of FĜH.

b Mark with an × the point which is equidistant from F and G
as well as the same distance from the lines FG and GH.

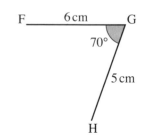

6 Draw the line QR then draw the locus of all the points P such that QP̂R = 90°.

Q

6 cm

R

7 Draw one copy of triangle PQR and show on it:

a the perpendicular bisector of QR.

b the bisector of PR̂Q.

c the locus of points nearer to PR than to QR *and* nearer to R than to Q.

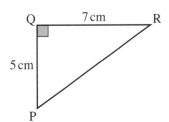

TASK E17.1 — **Main Book Page 547**

Remember: Learn! $\sin 0° = 0$ $\cos 0° = 1$ $\tan 0° = 0$

$\sin 90° = 1$ $\cos 90° = 0$

1 **a** Draw a graph of $y = \sin \theta$ for values of θ from 0° to 360° using intervals of 30°.

Use the graph to decide which of the statements below are true:

b $\sin 150° = \sin 60°$ **c** $\sin 330° = -\sin 30°$

d $\sin 225° = \sin 45°$ **e** $\sin 135° = \sin 45°$

2 This is part of the graph of $y = \cos x$.
Write down the co-ordinates of the points A, B, C and D.

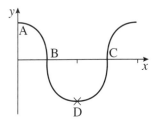

3 Look at the graph in question **2**. *Explain* why cos 240° cannot equal cos 60°.

4 Write down the lowest possible value of cos x.

5 Write down the greatest possible value of sin x.

6 How often does the sine curve repeat itself?

7 By considering the graph of $y = \tan x$ between values of x from 0° to 720°, how many times will the value of tan x equal 2·5?

TASK E17.2 ──────────────────── **Main Book Page 549**

Use the symmetry of the graphs of $y = \sin x$ and $y = \cos x$ to answer the following questions, giving each answer to the nearest degree.

1 If $\sin 53° = 0·799$, find another angle whose sine is $0·799$.

2 If $\cos 220° = -0·766$, find another angle whose cosine is $-0·766$.

3 Write down another angle which has the same cosine as
    a $39°$ **b** $47°$ **c** $171°$ **d** $108°$

4 Express the following in terms of the sine, cosine or tangent of an acute angle (the first one is done for you):
    a $\cos 320° = \cos 40°$ **b** $\cos 160°$ **c** $\sin 173°$ **d** $\cos 346°$
    a $\sin 294°$ **b** $\sin 219°$ **c** $\tan 247°$ **d** $\cos 162°$

5 Find two solutions between $0°$ and $360°$ for each of the following:
    a $\cos x = 0·7$ **b** $\sin x = 0·18$ **c** $\sin x = -0·93$
    d $\cos x = 0·84$ **e** $\cos x = -0·62$ **f** $\sin x = -0·447$

6 Solve $5\cos x = 1$ for x-values between $0°$ and $360°$.

7 Solve $2\sin x = -\sqrt{3}$ for x-values between $0°$ and $360°$.

8 Write down 3 values of x for which $\sin x = -0·5$.

9 This is part of the graph of
$y = 2 \cos x + 3$
Use your calculator to find
two *exact* values of x such that
$2 \cos x + 3 = 2$

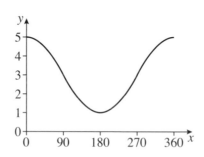

TASK E17.3 ──────────────────── **Main Book Page 553**

1 On squared paper, sketch
    a $f(x) + 1$
    b $-f(x)$
    c $f(x + 1)$
    d $f(x) - 1$

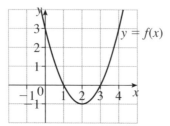

2 On squared paper, sketch

  a $g(x - 2)$

  b $g(x) + 3$

  c $g(-x)$

  d $g(x + 3)$

  g $-g(x)$

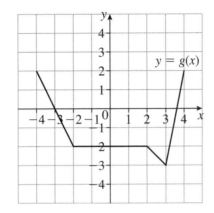

3 $f(x)$ has a minimum point at $(2, -1)$. Write down the co-ordinates of the minimum point for:

  a $f(x + 4)$ **b** $-f(x)$ **c** $f(x - 1)$ **d** $f(-x)$

4 **a** Sketch $y = \cos x$ for $0 \leqslant x \leqslant 360°$

  b Sketch $y = \cos (x + 90°)$

  c Sketch $y = 2 + \cos x$

5 Express $g(x)$ in terms of $f(x)$.

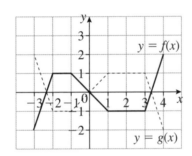

6 **a** Sketch the graph of $y = \dfrac{1}{x^2}$ for x-values from $x = -4$ to 4.

  b On the same axes, sketch $y = \dfrac{1}{x^2} + 2$

  c Sketch $y = -\dfrac{1}{x^2}$

TASK E17.4   **Main Book Page 555**

1 **a** Sketch $y = x^2 - 3$

  b On the same graph, sketch $y = (x + 2)^2 - 3$

2 **a** Sketch $y = 2^x$

  b On the same graph, sketch $y = 2^{-x}$

3 On squared paper, sketch

a $y = -f(x)$

b $y = -f(x) - 1$

c $y = f(-x)$

d $y = f(x) + 2$

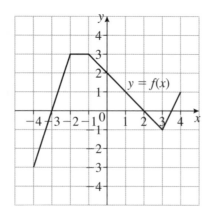

4 $g(x)$ has a minimum point at (2, 8). Write down the co-ordinates of the minimum point for:

a $g(x + 4)$ b $g(x + 4) - 3$ c $-g(x)$ d $6 - g(x)$

5 The graph of $y = \cos x$ is reflected in the x-axis then translated through $\begin{pmatrix} 0 \\ 3 \end{pmatrix}$.
Write down the equation of the new curve drawn.

6 Write down the real roots
for each of the following:

a $f(x) = 0$ b $f(x - 2) = 0$

c $f(-x) = 0$ d $f(x + 4) = 0$

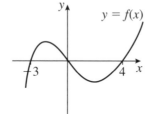

7

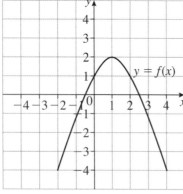

a On squared paper, sketch $y = f(x + 2)$

b Solve $f(x + 2) = 0$

c Solve $f(-x) = 0$

8 The graph of $y = (x + 1)^2 - 3(x + 1)$ is drawn by using the graph of $y = x^2 - 3x$.
Describe the transformation.

9 a Sketch $y = \tan x$ for $x = 0°$ to $360°$.

b Find the real roots of $\tan x = 0$

c Sketch $y = \tan(x - 90°)$

10 $y = f(x)$ has its vertex at $(-1, -3)$.
Write down the co-ordinates of the vertex for

a $y = f(x) - 1$　　　　**b** $y = f(-x) + 2$　　　　**c** $y = 3 - f(x)$　　　　**d** $y = f(x - 1) + 4$

GEOMETRY 6　　　　18

TASK M18.1 ———————————————— **Main Book Page 566**

1 Draw and label the plan and a side elevation for:

a a cuboid　　　　　　　　　　　　　　**b** a cone

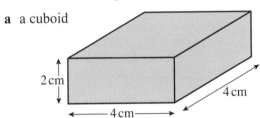
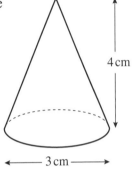

2 How many more cubes are
needed to make this shape
into a cuboid?

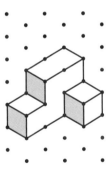

3 Draw this object from
a *different view*.

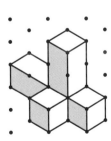

4 You are given the plan and two elevations of an object. Draw each object (on isometric paper if you wish to).

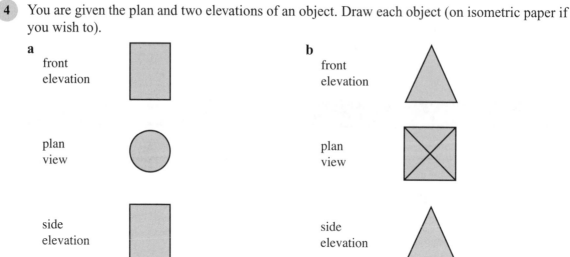

5 Two objects are made with 1 cm cubes. Their plans and elevations are shown below. How many cubes are used to make each solid?

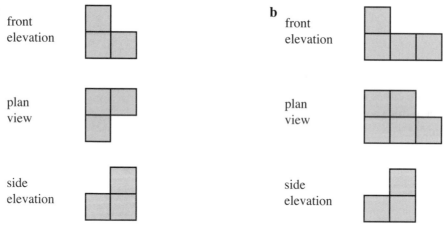

6 Draw a front elevation, plan view and side elevation of each solid below:

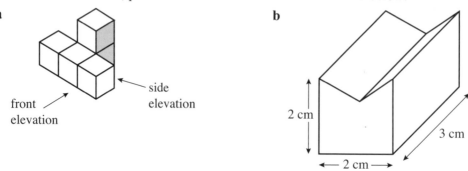

1 4 rabbits escape from their run and race off in the directions shown. On what bearing does each rabbit race?

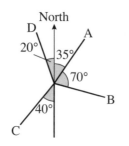

Remember: a bearing is measured clockwise from the North

2 A ship P sails from a harbour on a bearing of 125° for 18 km. A ship Q sails from the same harbour on a bearing of 230° for 12 km. Make a scale drawing using a scale of 1 cm for every 3 km. Write down how far apart the 2 ships are now.

3 Use a protractor to measure the bearing of:

   a Elton *from Saxley*

   b Elton *from Baghill*

   c Saxley *from Baghill*

   d Baghill *from Elton*

   e Saxley *from Elton*

   f Baghill *from Saxley*

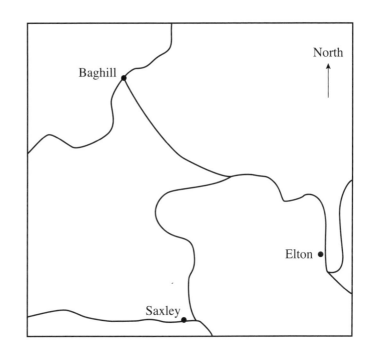

Note – the remaining questions need to be calculated. Do not use a protractor. Give answers to one decimal place when appropriate.

4 A plane flies 80 km north and 47 km west. What is the bearing from its original position to its new position?

5 Ken runs 5 km east from his home then 8 km north. On what bearing is he to run home if he is to take the shortest route?

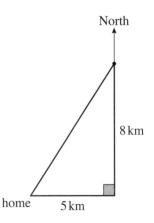

6 B is on a bearing of 305° from C.
a Find the length of BD.
b Find the bearing of A from B if AD = 4 km.

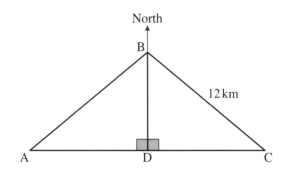

7 Find the bearing of:
a P from Q
b R from Q

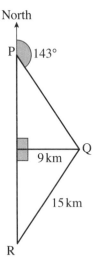

TASK M18.3 ——————————————————————— **Main Book Page 572**

Give answers in this Exercise to one decimal place when appropriate.

1 Ben is standing 90 m from the foot of a flagpole. The flagpole is 11 m tall. What is the angle of elevation of the top of the flagpole from Ben?

2 Rosa is standing on the top of a hill looking down at her village. The angle of depression of the top of her house is 7°. If she is 163 m higher than the top of her house, what is the horizontal distance of Rosa from her house?

3 Harry is standing on top of a castle keep, 29 m tall. A friend is standing on the ground below, 70 m from the foot of the castle keep. What is the angle of depression of the friend from Harry?

4 A camera is placed on a table to film a church. The angle of elevation from the camera to the top of a flagpole on the church tower is 5°. Using the measurements shown, what is the horizontal distance from the flagpole to the camera?

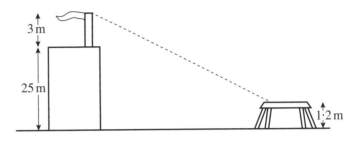

5 The angle of elevation of a bird from an observation point on the ground is 6·7°. If the horizontal distance of the bird from the observation point is 230 m, how high is the bird above the observation point?

6 The angles of elevation of the front of two tall buildings from a point A are shown in the diagram opposite. What is the difference in the heights of the two buildings?

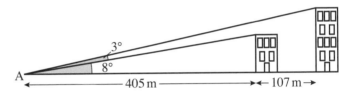

7 A telegraph pole stands on a line joining two points P and Q on the ground. The telegraph pole is 9 m tall. The angle of depression of the top of the pole to point P is 4°. The angle of depression of the top of the pole to point Q is 7°. What is the horizontal distance between P and Q?

8 A stone pillar is cylindrical with base diameter 40 cm. A point P is 10 m from the base of the pillar. The angle of elevation of the top of the pillar from P is 17°. The density of the stone is 2·7 tonnes/m³. Calculate the mass of the stone pillar.

TASK M18.4 — **Main Book Page 574**

You may use a calculator.

1 a A has co-ordinates (0, 4, 5). Write down the co-ordinates of B, C, D, E, F and G.

b Write down the co-ordinates of the midpoint of edge AB.

c Work out the total surface area of the cuboid ABCDEOFG.

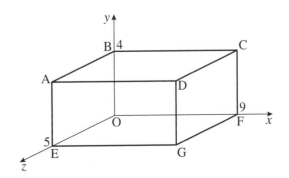

2 Each side of this cube is 2 units long.

  a Write down the co-ordinates of the vertices (corners) O, P, Q, R, S, T, U and V.

  b Calculate the length of QU.

  c Write down the co-ordinates of the centre of this cuboid.

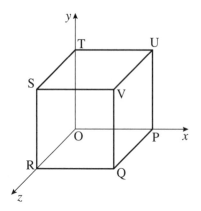

3 OABCDE is a triangular prism. The perpendicular height of triangle ABE is 8 units.

  a Write down the co-ordinates of the vertices O, A, B, C, D, E.

  b Find the co-ordinates of the midpoint of the diagonal AC.

  c Calculate the total surface area of the triangular prism.

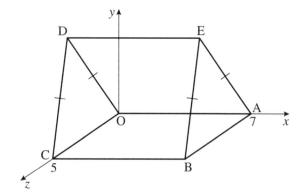

4 OPQRV is a rectangular-based pyramid. V is directly below the centre of the rectangular base. The pyramid has a height of 13 units. Write down the co-ordinates of O, P, Q, R, V.

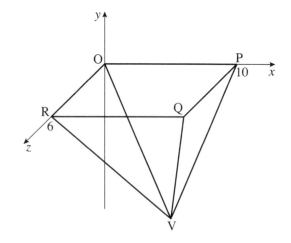

TASK E18.1 ──────────────────────────────── **Main Book Page 579**

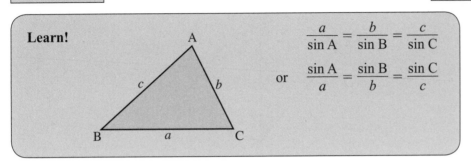

Learn!

$$\frac{a}{\sin A} = \frac{b}{\sin B} = \frac{c}{\sin C}$$

or

$$\frac{\sin A}{a} = \frac{\sin B}{b} = \frac{\sin C}{c}$$

Use a calculator and give all answers to 3 significant figures.

Find the value of each letter in questions **1** to **6** .

1
2
3

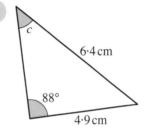

4
5
6

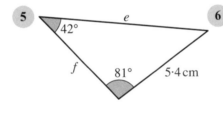
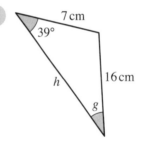

7 In triangle KLM, KM = 6·8 cm, KL̂M = 78° and MK̂L = 34°.
Find the perimeter of triangle KLM.

8 Maddlestone is 28 km due north of Kenton. Howick is on a bearing of 137° from Maddlestone and Howick is on a bearing of 067° from Kenton. Find the shortest distance from Kenton to Howick.

9 Calculate the area of quadrilateral ABCD.

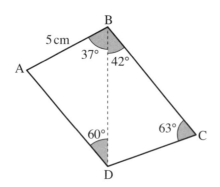

TASK E18.2 ——————————————————— **Main Book Page 581**

Learn!

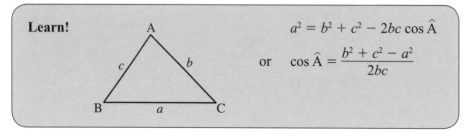

$$a^2 = b^2 + c^2 - 2bc \cos \hat{A}$$

or $\cos \hat{A} = \dfrac{b^2 + c^2 - a^2}{2bc}$

Use a calculator and give all answers to 3 significant figures.

Find the value of each letter in questions **1** to **3**.

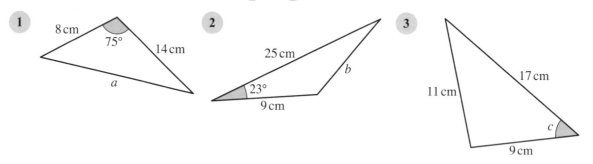

4 In triangle PQR, PQ = 32 cm, PR = 28 cm and QR = 21 cm.
Find the size of QP̂R.

5 A boat sails due North for 41 km then travels on a bearing of 218° for 23 km.
The boat then sails back to its starting position. Find the total distance travelled by the boat.

6 Alan is 14 km due east of Davina. Alan walks on a bearing of $x°$ and Davina walks on a bearing of $y°$. They meet at a more southerly point when Alan has walked 7 km and Davina has walked 10 km. Find x and y.

7 Find the perimeter of triangle ABC.

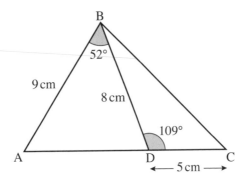

TASK E18.3 ──────────────────── **Main Book Page 583**

> **Remember:**
>
> area $= \frac{1}{2}ab \sin \hat{C}$

Use a calculator and give all answers to 3 significant figures when appropriate.

Find the value of each letter in questions **1** to **3**

1

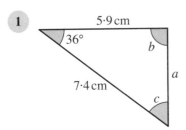

2

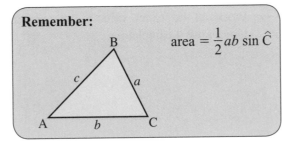

3

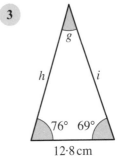

4 In triangle ABC, AB = 15·1 cm, BC = 29·7 cm and AC = 19·6 cm.
Find the area of triangle ABC.

5 Balloon A travels 15 km on a bearing of 029°.
Balloon B travels 39 km on a bearing of 043°.
a How far apart are the balloons now?
b On what bearing would balloon A have to travel in order to reach the position of balloon B?

6 Hanif walks 6 km on a bearing of 159° then 9 km on a bearing of 252°. On what bearing must Hanif walk to return to his starting point and how much further must he walk?

TASK E18.4 ──────────────────────────────── **Main Book Page 584**

1 Calculate the length QR.

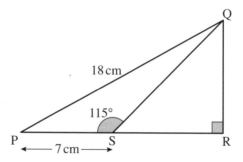

2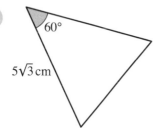

The area of the triangle opposite is 30 cm².

Work out the 'exact' value of the perimeter of the triangle.
Do *not* use a calculator.

3 A triangle PQR is such that QR is 3 cm longer than PQ.
$P\hat{Q}R = 120°$ and $PR = 3\sqrt{7}$ cm.

  a By letting $PQ = x$ cm, form a quadratic equation involving x.

  b Find the 'exact' perimeter of the triangle PQR.

4 If the area of triangle PRS is 127 cm²,
find the area of triangle PQR.

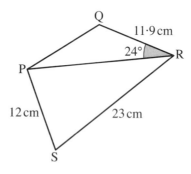

5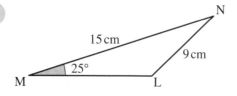

$M\hat{L}N$ is obtuse.

Work out the value of $M\hat{L}N$.

6

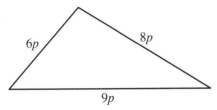

6p   8p

9p

Work out the largest angle in the triangle opposite.

7 Holly jogs at a speed of 6 mph. She leaves a point A on a bearing of 042° and jogs for $1\frac{1}{4}$ hours to a point B. She then travels for 1 hour 30 minutes on a bearing of 149° to a point C. She then runs directly back to point A. On what bearing does she jog from C to A and how long was her total journey (give the answer to the nearest minute)?

8 Comment on what the cosine rule effectively becomes when finding the length a if $\hat{A} = 90°$?

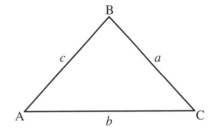

TASK E18.5 ──────────────────────── **Main Book Page 587**

Use a calculator and give all answers to 3 significant figures when appropriate.

1 This pyramid has a square base PQRS of side length 9 cm.

VM is vertical. M is the midpoint of PR.

Find

a the length of PM

b the height VM of the pyramid

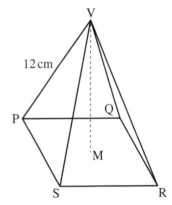

2 Find the following lengths in this cuboid.

a QS

b LS

c KR

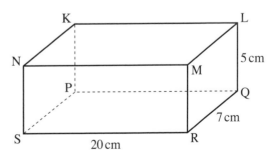

3 A man walks 30 m due West from the foot of an aerial mast which is 40 m high. He then walks 50 m North. How far is he from the top of the mast?

4 This pyramid has a rectangular base ABCD which is horizontal. The vertex P is directly above the centre of the rectangular base.

The perpendicular height of the pyramid is 27 cm.

Find

a AQ

b AP

c the area of the face PCD

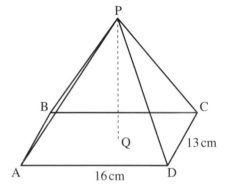

5 A cuboid is such that its height is 1 m longer than its width and its length is 2 m longer than its height.

If the longest diagonal in the cuboid is 6 m then find the width of the cuboid.

6 In the diagram opposite, D has co-ordinates (a, b, c).

M is the midpoint of DF.

N is the midpoint of BC.

Prove that MN $= \dfrac{1}{2} \sqrt{a^2 + b^2 + 4c^2}$.

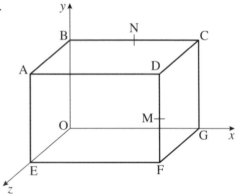

TASK E18.6 ———————————————————— **Main Book Page 591**

Use a calculator and give all answers to 3 significant figures.

1 PQRSTUVW is a cuboid. Find

a QV **b** QV̂U

c WU **d** WÛV

e QW **f** QŴU

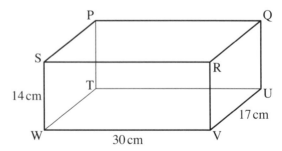

2 BC is perpendicular to CD.

Find

a AC

b BÂC

c CD

d the angle between BD and the plane ACD

e Find the total surface area of the pyramid ABCD.

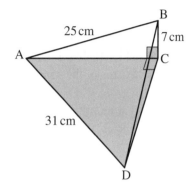

3 This pyramid has a rectangular base ABCD. VM is vertical. M is the midpoint of AC. Find

a BM

b VM

c the angle between VB and the plane ABCD

d BV̂C

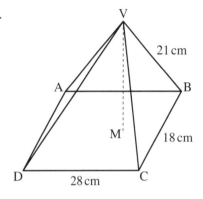

4

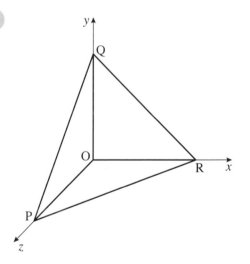

The vertices of the pyramid OPQR are O(0, 0, 0), P(0, 0, $2\sqrt{3}$), Q(0, 2, 0) and R($2\sqrt{2}$, 0, 0).

Claire works out that cos PQ̂R = $\frac{1}{6}\sqrt{3}$.

Is she correct? Show all your working out.

5 This diagram represents the roof of a house.

ABCD is horizontal with AB = 10 m and BC = 26 m. EF is horizontal. EF is 20 m long and 2 m above the horizontal plane ABCD.

AEB and DFC make the same angle with ABCD. BCFE and ADFE make the same angle with ABCD.

N is in the plane ABCD and is vertically below E. M is the midpoint of AB. X is the point on BC such that NX̂C is a right angle.

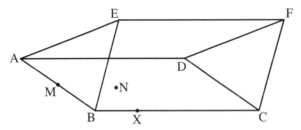

a Write down the lengths of EN and MN.

b Find the angle between EM and the plane ABCD.

c Calculate the length NC.

d Find the angle which the line EC makes with the plane ABCD.

6

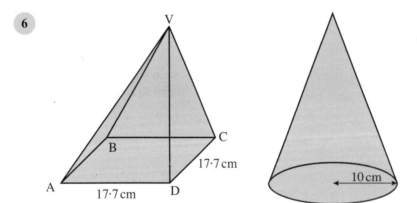

The square based pyramid above has the same perpendicular height as the cone. Vertex V is vertically above the midpoint of AC. Calculate the value of VÂD if the 'exact' curved surface area of the cone is 260π cm².